A NEW
HEALTHY YOU!

Gluten Free

igloobooks

igloobooks

Published in 2017
by Igloo Books Ltd
Cottage Farm
Sywell
NN6 0BJ
www.igloobooks.com

Cover images: (bc) Dorling Kindersley: Charlotte Tolhurst / © Getty images
Additional cover and interior imagery: © istock / Getty images

HUN001 1017
2 4 6 8 10 9 7 5 3 1
ISBN 978-1-78810-619-1

Cover designed by Nicholas Gage
Edited by Jasmin Peppiatt

Printed and manufactured in China

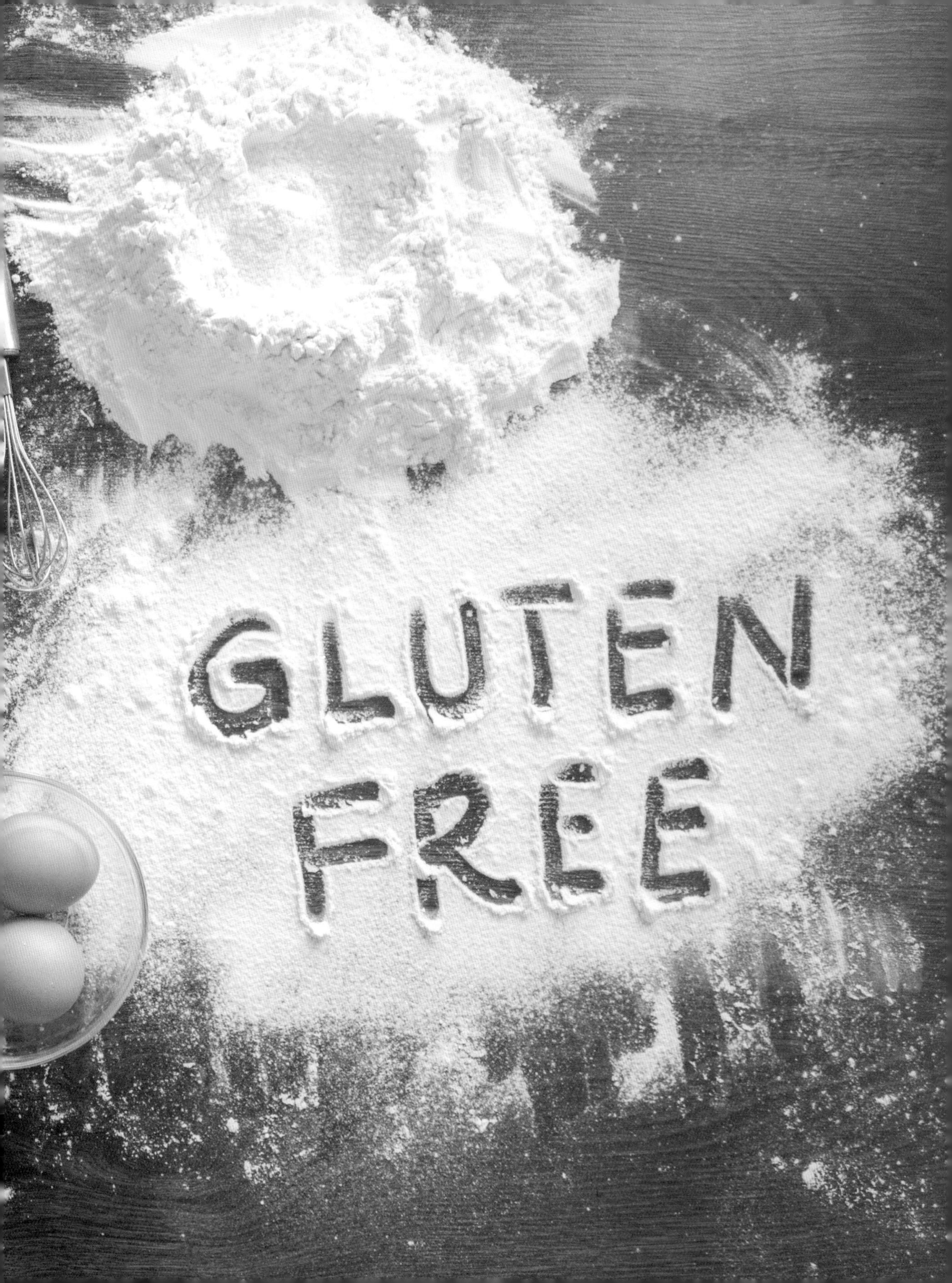
GLUTEN
FREE

Contents

Introduction

Recipes

Meal plans and diary

Introduction

Sometimes it seems that there are regular stories in the news about a food that we should avoid. First, it was fat and cholesterol, then carbohydrates, then sugar and alcohol. Now there's a lot of talk about going gluten-free. Celebrities are doing it, and most supermarkets now have a well-stocked gluten-free section. But what exactly is gluten and why are so many people trying to avoid it?

What is gluten?

In simple terms, gluten is a general name for the proteins found in wheat and some other grains. Its name comes from the Latin word for 'glue' and it is what makes pastry puffy and pizza dough stretchy. It can be found in wheat, barley, rye, most oats and the foods that contain them – such as bread, pasta, beer and cereals. For a few people, eating gluten can cause serious health problems but, for most people, eating it has no adverse effects.

Healthy living

Many people who have gone gluten-free are quick to sing its praises. Eliminating gluten has helped them lose weight, they say, as well as giving them more energy and a clearer mind. Going gluten-free can be tricky, since it is found in so many popular foods. But for some people, it's worth the trouble. Could gluten-free be the right diet for you?

GLUTEN-FREE CHAMPION
The tennis player Novak Djokovic does not have coeliac disease, but he believes that an intolerance to gluten led to a lack of energy and symptoms similar to asthma. In 2011, he cut out gluten from his diet entirely and the results were staggering. He says that he felt quicker, lighter, and had lots more energy.

Why go gluten-free?

Some people have no choice about going gluten-free. They may suffer from coeliac disease, a lifelong autoimmune disorder. A coeliac sufferer's immune system reacts to gluten by attacking the lining of the small intestine. Over time, this damage can leave the small intestine unable to efficiently absorb nutrients from food, leaving the person malnourished.

For somebody with coeliac disease, eating gluten may cause symptoms including bloating, diarrhoea, nausea, fatigue, headaches and weight loss. Over the long term, it may lead to osteoporosis and anaemia, as well as some cancers. There is no cure for coeliac disease, but switching to a strict gluten-free diet will eliminate the symptoms and avoid damage to the small intestine.

Gluten sensitivity

Some people who do not have coeliac disease are still affected by eating gluten – this is called non-coeliac gluten sensitivity. It is still not completely understood by scientists. The symptoms are mostly the same as for a coeliac disease sufferer, but no damage occurs to the small intestine if gluten is eaten. This condition is currently being researched and there is no specific test to diagnose it. However, many people who have tested negative for coeliac disease see an improvement in their gut symptoms after cutting out gluten from their diet.

WHEAT ALLERGY

Some people are allergic to wheat. When they eat it, their immune system reacts by producing antibodies. These can cause symptoms such as watery eyes, itching, rashes, coughing, breathing difficulties, headaches and nausea. A wheat allergy can be diagnosed by a doctor by carrying out a skin-prick test. Foods labelled 'gluten-free' are not always safe for people with wheat allergies, as the food may still contain wheat, even though the gluten has been removed.

Making a choice

Coeliac disease probably affects about one in 100 people, though many of these people are undiagnosed. Wheat allergy affects even fewer – mainly children will outgrow it by the time they reach adulthood. There are no reliable statistics for people with non-coeliac gluten sensitivity. Even so, that leaves a small slice of the population with a medical reason to avoid gluten. So why are so many otherwise healthy people going gluten-free?

Is it healthier?

There is a perception that going gluten-free is a healthier way of living. Celebrities and sports stars who have given up gluten are a great advertisement for this – they are successful and they look great! With the range of gluten-free foods that are now available, it has never been easier to give it a try. But so far, scientists have not found evidence that gluten is harmful or fattening, except for the minority of people with a sensitivity or allergy.

Out with the bad...

One reason to give up gluten is that it often leads to a healthier diet overall. Many foods that contain gluten, such as cakes and biscuits, are unhealthy in other ways – high in fat and sugar, for example. Going gluten-free means taking a look at your diet to see where changes can be made. Often, you end up replacing foods containing gluten with healthier alternatives, such as lean proteins and vegetables, which can only be a good thing!

GLUTEN AND CARBS

Many popular diets are focused around reducing carbohydrate intake, especially so-called 'empty carbs', such as those found in white bread, sugar, white rice, cakes and biscuits. A lot of people are able to lose weight by replacing these foods in their diet with whole grains, vegetables and lean meats. Many of the foods that contain gluten are also high in carbohydrates, so eliminating them may help you lose weight.

Before you start

If you're planning to go gluten-free because you want a healthier diet overall, great! But, if you think you may have coeliac disease or a wheat allergy, it is very important to get a proper diagnosis from a doctor.

Here is a list of symptoms that may indicate coeliac disease:

- nausea and vomiting
- persistent diarrhoea, constipation or wind
- cramping or bloating
- tiredness and headaches

- unexplained weight loss
- skin rash
- numbness and tingling in the hands and feet

Make a note of any symptoms, keep a food diary and ensure that you see your GP before cutting out gluten from your diet. Many of these symptoms can also be caused by other conditions, such as irritable bowel syndrome. Your GP will usually take a blood sample to test for antibodies that can indicate coeliac disease. If the test is positive, you will usually be referred to a specialist for a definite diagnosis.

A helping hand

It is important to know if you have coeliac disease and, once you are diagnosed, your GP will be able to offer support, including referrals to specialist dietitians.

The only treatment for coeliac disease is to go gluten-free permanently. This can be a difficult adjustment, but a dietitian will be able to help. They will guide you on which foods you can and cannot eat and will often provide you with useful meal ideas to ensure that you are consuming a good amount of vitamins and minerals.

Stay safe

Even if you don't think you have coeliac disease or a wheat allergy, it is always a good idea to talk to your GP before starting a new diet.

They will be able to offer advice on the safest and healthiest way to lose weight, and they can provide information about achieving a more balanced diet.

GETTING SUPPORT

If you are diagnosed with coeliac disease, you shouldn't feel alone. There are numerous organisations and charities focused on helping people with the condition. Your GP can put you in touch with people that can offer information, advice and support.

A balanced diet

No matter what diet you choose to follow, it's important to give your body the right balance of nutrients. Your body doesn't actually need gluten, so there are no harmful effects as a result of giving it up. However, many of the foods that contain gluten also contain other vital nutrients, such as fibre, iron, folic acid and B vitamins. If you are cutting gluten-based foods out of your diet, you will need to find another source of these important nutrients.

As with any diet, the key is to eat a balance of different types of food. For example, everyone should eat at least five portions of fruit and vegetables each day and this won't change on a gluten-free diet. Fruit and vegetables are naturally gluten-free and they are packed with vitamins and minerals. For sources of protein, stick to pulses, nuts, leafy greens, lean meats and fish. Try to keep salt, sugar and fat to a minimum.

Grains and starches

Grains and starchy foods are usually the trickiest part of a gluten-free diet. Cutting out wheat eliminates a big category of foods from your diet, but there are others to replace them. You can replace wheat, rye and barley with rice, potatoes, sweet potatoes and a variety of naturally gluten-free grains. You can also buy gluten-free versions of many common foods, such as bread, cereal and pasta.

FIBRE

On a gluten-free diet, you need to make sure that you get enough fibre. Fibre passes through the body without being absorbed, and it is found in many wholegrain cereals, including wheat. Cutting out wheat, rye and barley may mean you are no longer getting enough fibre. Foods such as brown rice, corn, peas, beans and lentils are all good sources of fibre. Try to include these foods in your gluten-free diet.

What to eat

If you make a list of all the different foods you eat that contain wheat, the thought of cutting them out may seem impossible. But there are a lot of delicious substitutes for these foods, and most of them have become more easily available in the last decade. 'Gluten-free' doesn't have to mean 'grain-free'!

What grains can I eat?

On this diet, you can safely eat brown rice and sweetcorn (even popcorn!), as well as quinoa, buckwheat, millet, sorghum and amaranth. Oats are naturally gluten-free as well, but they are often contaminated with gluten during processing, so make sure you choose those that are marked as 'gluten-free'. These grains are a good source of energy, and they also provide iron, calcium, fibre and B vitamins. If you've never cooked with these grains before, don't panic – this book has recipes that will help you and inspire you to try new gluten-free dishes.

Making changes

The great thing about going gluten-free is that it doesn't necessarily mean you have to eat less, you're just eating slightly differently. By replacing refined foods – such as white bread – with healthier alternatives, you'll be doing your body a lot of good. Focusing on whole foods – such as lean meats, fish, vegetables and whole grains – is the foundation of a healthy diet.

IRON

Iron is important in any diet, but even more so for people with coeliac disease. Damage to the small intestine can mean that the body doesn't absorb iron very well, leaving them anaemic. Even if you don't have coeliac disease, you need to watch your iron intake. Wheat flour is usually enriched with iron, but gluten-free flours aren't. To make sure you are getting enough iron, eat red meat, liver, leafy green vegetables, pulses, dried fruits, nuts and seeds.

Which foods contain gluten?

It's obvious that some foods contain gluten – bagels, for example, or croissants – but a lot of gluten is 'hiding' in places where you might not expect to find it, such as in packaged sauces or dressings. When in doubt, always check the label.

In addition to bread and pasta, you will need to avoid couscous, flour tortillas, most noodles, muffins, pastries, many breakfast cereals, biscuits (sweet and savoury) and cakes. These are all usually made with wheat, although gluten-free versions are available. You'll also need to cut out various other foods that contain gluten: beer, some gravy, many salad dressings, breadcrumbs and croutons, anything cooked in batter and barley water, to name a few.

GLUTEN-FREE ON A BUDGET

Gluten-free products, such as bread, may save time, but they can also cost three or four times as much as the wheat-based version. However, going gluten-free does not have to break the bank! By cooking as much as possible yourself, you will save money and have the confidence that comes from knowing exactly what you're eating. You can make big batches of soup, chilli or curry and freeze individual portions for when you're in a hurry.

Hidden gluten

Processed foods often contain gluten because food manufacturers use it as an additive. Gluten can be added to foods to stabilise or thicken them and to keep them from separating. Be especially wary of tinned meat products, condiments, pasta sauces, barbecue sauces, soy sauce, processed meats, stock and anything containing gravy.

Reading food labels

To go gluten-free, you'll have to become an expert at reading food labels. Gluten can be part of nearly every food, but it's not always easy to spot on the label. Some foods are designed to be gluten-free and they will have a prominent label saying so. Some foods display the 'crossed grain' symbol developed by the charity Coeliac UK, which shows that a product is certified gluten-free.

What to look for

There are strict laws controlling the way that food is labelled. Only foods that contain less than 20 parts per million of gluten can be labelled 'gluten-free'. These include flour substitute products, such as breads and crackers, as well as processed foods that are naturally gluten-free, including soups and crisps.

Other labels

There is another category, 'very low gluten', for substitute products containing between 20 and 100 parts per million, although this is rare. Some foods may carry a label stating 'no gluten-containing ingredients'. The use of this term isn't covered by law, but is used by manufacturers and caterers to identify foods made with ingredients that don't contain gluten, where they are confident that there has been no cross contamination.

If a product is clearly labelled 'gluten-free', it makes life much easier! The use of this term is strictly regulated, so you can be confident that these products are safe. On products without this label, you have to look carefully to find the gluten listed.

CROSS CONTAMINATION

Any time that a gluten-free food comes into contact with gluten, it is called 'cross contamination'. This can happen at nearly any point from farm to plate: during harvesting, transport, processing, cooking and serving. Cross contamination is common in factories where many different food types are processed, and this is why people with coeliac disease avoid eating regular oats. Cross contamination can even be a problem at home if you don't properly clean your pans, utensils and chopping boards after preparing foods with gluten.

Hidden gluten

If a product uses a gluten-containing cereal as an ingredient, it must be listed in the ingredients list, no matter how little of it is used. These include wheat, barley, rye, oats, spelt and khorasan wheat (sometimes called Kamut®).

There are a host of other ingredients that are derived from gluten-containing cereals. Keep your eyes peeled for terms such as malt extract and brewer's yeast. To make things even trickier, there are many different varieties of wheat. These types of wheat include bulgar wheat and durum wheat.

Energy	2750kJ 650kcal
Protein	3.4g
Carbohydrate	4.7g
of which sugars	4.7g
Fat	3.6g
of which saturates	2.3g
...urates	1.0g

Gluten-free but fattening

Don't forget to check the other nutritional information as well, including sugar, salt and fat content. Foods that are specifically designed to be gluten-free often have extra sugar and fat added to make up for the missing gluten. Try making your own gluten-free bread or bagels. With the right recipe, it's not difficult and you'll save money.

NEW RULES

New laws came into place in 2014 that affect the labelling of food. Any food considered to be an allergen (which includes gluten-containing ingredients) must now be emphasised in the ingredients list. They might be in italics, underlined or in bold type – anything that makes them stand out. This makes it easier to identify products containing gluten.

Eating out

Having a meal out is a fantastic treat, but it can be tricky if you are on a gluten-free diet. Luckily, in the past few years, restaurants have become much more aware of people's need for gluten-free food. Many menus list any dishes that are gluten-free, and kitchen staff are often more informed about how to avoid cross contamination during food preparation.

PLAN AHEAD

If you're worried, check out the restaurant's website before you go. Many chain restaurants have allergy information on their websites. You could also call and speak to someone before you go. By talking to staff about their procedures, you can gauge their level of awareness. For example, if they list their chips as gluten-free, ask them if the oil used for chips is also used to fry battered foods – the flour or breadcrumbs contaminate the oil.

Here are a few tips for enjoying your meal with confidence:

- Arrive with a positive mindset, getting excited about what you can eat, rather than focusing on what you can't.

- Tell your server that you are on a gluten-free diet. He or she may be able to make suggestions of suitable dishes. So many people are eating gluten-free that they will be used to being asked about the menu options!

- Stick to foods that are naturally gluten-free, such as potatoes, meat, fish and vegetables.

- Don't be afraid to order your food exactly as you want it. Sauces and salad dressings are often hidden sources of gluten. If in any doubt, ask to have it without.

- Some food types, such as Indian and Thai, are usually made with mainly gluten-free ingredients, so these can be good options. Always check the ingredients with your server to make sure.

Losing weight

Some people have no choice about going gluten-free, but many others adopt the diet in order to lose weight and feel healthier. The truth is that – unless you suffer from coeliac disease, a wheat allergy or gluten sensitivity – there is no evidence that eating gluten is harmful or fattening. However, many people do lose weight and look fabulous on a gluten-free diet. How do they do it?

Cutting out the bad

Many of us eat a diet that relies heavily on wheat-based products. This is not necessarily a bad thing – after all, whole grains are an important source of fibre and other nutrients. But there are a lot of wheat-based foods that are less healthy. Biscuits, cakes and pastries are obvious examples of this, but what about that slice of lovely wholegrain bread you had for breakfast, slathered with fatty butter and sugary jam? Or the floury batter on your deep-fried fish and chips?

Changing diet

By cutting out wheat, many people find that their whole diet changes. It's not about
replacing their normal food with like-for-like gluten-free substitutes, which are often
high in fat or sugar and nearly always more expensive. Instead, they switch to grains such
as brown rice, which pack a big nutritional punch while containing relatively few calories.
They eat more vegetables and pulses and pay close attention to exactly what they're eating.
This balanced approach can make you healthier overall and help you lose weight.

THE BIG PICTURE

Just because a food is gluten-free doesn't necessarily mean that it is healthy. After all,
a gluten-free cake is still a cake! You need to look at all the nutritional content of a food
before choosing it: fat, sugar, fibre, carbohydrates, vitamins and more.

Being active, staying safe

Going gluten-free is a great start, but any plan to lose weight must be more than just a new food regime. You need to stay active to burn off calories as well as improve your overall health and fitness.

If you reduce your fat and sugar intake as part of your gluten-free diet, you will probably lose weight and, if you increase the amount of exercise you do, you will lose even more!

Keep it simple

Many people are reluctant to start an exercise programme because they think they need to join the gym or get a new workout wardrobe. They get concerned about how much time it will take up out of their busy schedule or how much a gym membership may cost. But, remember that you don't need to break a sweat to get the benefit from exercise.

If you keep moving for several hours throughout the day, you will get just as much benefit as you would from a 30-minute jog. Take the stairs whenever you can, park at the far end of the supermarket car park or get off the bus two or three stops earlier than usual. Over the course of a day, these little bits of exercise can add up!

The more the merrier

One of the most effective things you can do is to find a friend who's also trying to become more active. Having a friend to exercise with can keep you motivated and you're more likely to stick with it. It doesn't have to be a competition to see who can run for longer or do more crunches – instead, it can be a great opportunity for a chat!

SIDE BENEFITS

Keeping active is not just about losing weight! Regular exercise will strengthen muscles and bones, keep your heart healthy and reduce your risk of serious illnesses, such as diabetes or stroke. And, although it might sound crazy, regular exercise can also make you feel more energetic.

WARMING UP

Make sure that your body is ready before exercising. You need to gently stretch and warm up your muscles before an exercise session to reduce the risk of injury. Stretching can also improve your overall flexibility and muscle tone. Once you've finished exercising, some deep breathing, accompanied by more stretching, is a great way to cool down.

Step it up

Once you get into the swing of things with your new diet, you may feel like you have more energy. Well, now is the time to use it! Swimming is a fantastic way to burn calories. It is non-weight-bearing, so it puts less pressure on your joints. Walking, jogging and cycling are also great ways to burn calories while you're enjoying the fresh air and exploring your town, city or countryside. If the weather's bad and you're stuck indoors, you can burn calories doing the housework.

A family affair

If you have children, get them exercising with you! Take them to the park, but instead of sitting on a bench texting while they play, join in for some football, tag or hide and seek. If you have a dog, make a point of taking it for a walk or jog every day. If you don't, why not borrow one? You might be able to help an elderly neighbour who can't give their pet the exercise it needs.

Stay safe

If you're new to exercising, or you have any specific health conditions, it's best to talk to your GP, gym instructor or personal trainer before you start a fitness programme. They'll be able to offer support and advice on the best and safest ways to keep fit and lose weight.

Breakfasts and brunches

If you're used to starting your day with toast or cereal, breakfast can be one of the trickiest meals on a gluten-free diet. Supermarket shelves are full of gluten-free substitutes for bread, muffins and cereals, but these products are sometimes no healthier than the original version! Now is your chance to make a change and try something new.

Porridge, made from gluten-free oats, is a great start to the day. It will give you slow-burning energy that will keep you feeling fuller for longer. Alternatively, if you don't like to eat first thing in the morning, the recipes in this chapter can be eaten as a mid-morning meal instead.

From Waffles with Chocolate and Banana or Homemade Granola to Poached Mackerel with Egg and Frittatas, there is something for everyone in this chapter.

There is no need to worry about preparing a gluten-free breakfast, as this chapter will give you all the inspiration you need to get started with enjoying and experimenting with gluten-free food.

If you really can't give up your morning toast, use gluten-free wholegrain bread and spread, such as a soft cheese or refreshing mashed avocado. These provide nutrients without the sugar found in jam and other breakfast spreads.

Preparation time: **5 minutes**

Cooking time: **10 minutes**

Porridge with mixed dried fruit

50 g / 1 ½ oz / ½ cup gluten-free
  porridge oats

200 ml / 7 fl. oż / ¾ cup almond milk

1 tsp raw organic honey

25 g mixed dried fruit

1. In a heavy bottomed saucepan, heat the oats and milk over a medium heat, stirring regularly.

2. After 10 minutes, once thickened and once the oats are soft, stir in the honey to taste. Add a little more milk if you prefer the porridge runnier.

3. Pour into a serving bowl and top with the mixed dried fruits.

4. If desired, add further toppings such as chopped nuts.

SERVES: 4

Preparation time: **10 minutes**

Cooking time: **10 minutes**

Waffles with chocolate and banana

75 g / 2 ½ oz / ⅓ cup unsalted butter

2 large eggs

300 ml / 10 ½ fl. oz / 1 ¼ cups almond milk

225 g / 8 oz / 1 ½ cups gluten-free flour

2 tsp gluten-free baking powder

75 g / 2 ½ oz / ⅓ cup caster
(superfine) sugar

100 g / 3 ½ oz / ⅔ cup organic
dark chocolate

100 ml / 3 ½ fl. oz / ½ cup double
(heavy) cream

1 banana, sliced

75 g / 3 ½ oz fresh strawberries, halved

50 g / 1 ½ oz / ½ cup walnuts

1. Turn out your waffle iron to heat up.

2. In a small saucepan, melt the butter and set
   aside to cool.

3. Whisk together the eggs and milk until
   combined. Add the flour, baking powder,
   sugar and most of the melted butter,
   continuing to whisk until a light batter forms.

4. Brush the waffle iron with the remaining
   butter and cook the waffles in batches,
   then place into a low oven to keep warm.

5. Break 80 g of the chocolate into a bowl.
   Gently warm the cream until not quite
   bubbling and pour over the chocolate while
   whisking continuously until thick.

6. Spread the chocolate mix onto the waffles and
   top with the fruit and nuts.

7. Grate over the remaining chocolate and serve.

SERVES: 6-8

Preparation time: **10 minutes**

Cooking time: **20 minutes**

Homemade granola

150 g / 5 oz / ½ cup pure maple syrup

2 tbsp raw honey

1 tsp vanilla extract

300 g / 10 ½ oz / 3 cups gluten-free whole
    rolled oats

100 g / 3 ½ oz/ ¾ cup pecan pieces

100 g / 3 ½ oz / ½ cup dried cranberries

200 g / 7 oz / 1 cup natural fat-free yogurt

strawberries and blueberries to serve

1. Preheat the oven to 150°C (130°C fan) / 300F /
   gas 2. Mix together the syrup, honey, and
   vanilla extract in a large bowl. Mix in the
   oats and pecan pieces until combined.

2. Tip the granola mixture onto a baking tray
   and spread evenly (use two trays if required).
   Place in the oven to bake for 20 minutes,
   turning the mixture over once during cooking.

3. Remove from the oven and leave to cool.
   Once cooled, mix in the dried fruits and store
   in an airtight container for up to 1 month.

4. To serve, fill a bowl with the yogurt and top
   with a handful of granola and the chopped
   fresh berries.

SERVES : 2

Preparation time: **10 minutes**

Freezing time: **at least 1 hour**

Banana mango smoothie

1 banana

1 mango

1 lime, juiced

100 ml / 3 ½ fl. oz / ½ cup almond milk

a sprig of mint

1. Peel and chop up the banana. Place into a sealable bag and place into the freezer until frozen, at least an hour or overnight, if possible.

2. Peel the mango and chop up into small chunks. Place into the cup of a high-powered blender with the frozen banana, lime juice and almond milk. Blend according to the manufacturer's guidelines until combined and smooth.

3. Pour into a glass and garnish with a sprig of mint.

SERVES: 4-6

Preparation time: **15 minutes**

Cooking time: **45 minutes**

Frittata

30 g / 1 oz butter

1 tsp olive oil

2 potatoes, peeled and cut into cubes

200 g / 7 oz cubetti di pancetta

1 red pepper, deseeded and sliced

6 spring onions (scallions), sliced

6 eggs

salt and black pepper

100 g / 3 ½ oz / 1 cup cheddar cheese, grated

1. In a large frying pan, heat the oil and butter together over a medium heat. Add the potatoes and fry for 20 minutes, turning occasionally. The edges should be crisping up and they will be softened.

2. Add the pancetta to the pan and cook for a further 5 minutes followed by the pepper. Continue to fry for 5 minutes, adding half the onion for a couple of minutes.

3. Beat the eggs together with half the cheese and season with salt and black pepper. Pour into the pan and gently swill around until the egg has filled the pan and coated the other ingredients. Leave to cook for around 10 minutes until the bottom is cooked and the surface is still a little runny. While the frittata is cooking, preheat the grill.

4. Sprinkle the remaining cheese and spring onions over the surface of the frittata and place under the grill until browned and cooked.

5. Cut into wedges and serve with a fresh salad.

SERVES: 2

Preparation time: **10 minutes**

Cooking time: **10 minutes**

Strawberry pancakes

200 g / 7 oz / 1 ⅓ cups buckwheat flour

30 g / 1 oz caster (superfine) sugar

1 tsp gluten-free baking powder

½ tsp xanthan gum

1 egg

100 ml / 3 ½ fl. oz / ⅔ cup milk

1 tbsp oil

100 g / 3 ½ oz fresh strawberries

a drizzle of maple syrup

1. In a large mixing bowl, combine the flour, sugar, baking powder and xanthan gum. Mix together before adding the egg and milk. Whisk to form a thick batter, about the consistency of double cream. Leave to stand for 5 minutes.

2. In a small frying pan, heat some oil over a medium heat. Once hot, add a ladleful of the batter mix and fry until bubbles popping on the surface leave a hole in the batter. Flip and cook on the other side for a further minute. Repeat until all the pancakes are cooked. You can keep cooked ones warm in the oven.

3. Cut the strawberries into halves or leave whole. Add the pancakes to plates and top with the strawberries and maple syrup.

4. This makes a fantastic breakfast. You can top the pancakes with different fruits and berries or even chocolate sauce.

SERVES: 1

Preparation time: **10 minutes**

Cocoa smoothie bowl

1 banana

250 ml / 9 fl. oz / 1 cup Greek yogurt

1 tsp cocoa powder

1 tbsp granola

1 tsp dried fruits

1. Place ¾ of the banana into a blender with the yogurt and cocoa. Blend until smooth and combined.

2. Pour the blended mixture into a serving bowl.

3. Slice the remaining banana and add to the bowl. Spoon over the granola and dried fruit with an additional dusting of cocoa powder if desired.

SERVES : 2

Preparation time: **10 minutes**
Cooking time: **15 minutes**

Poached mackerel with egg

1 large free range egg
2 mackerel fillets
2 bay leaves
1 tsp black peppercorns
100 g / 3 ½ oz baby spinach, washed
sea salt and cracked black pepper
gluten-free bread, toasted, to serve

1. Place the egg into a pan of cold water. Bring to the boil and cook for 3 minutes before draining. Refill the pan with cold water to stop the egg cooking. Once cooled, peel the egg.

2. Pin bone the mackerel using fish tweezers. Rinse and pat dry with kitchen paper.

3. Half fill a large flat pan with high sides with water. Add the bay leaves and peppercorns and bring up to not quite boiling. Add the fish and poach for 8-10 minutes turning once. Carefully remove using a fish slice and place skin side up on some kitchen paper.

4. To serve, place the spinach leaves onto a plate. Cut the egg in half, placing half on each plate. Remove the skin from the fish and lightly flake the flesh before adding to the plates.

5. Season with salt and black pepper and serve with gluten-free toast.

Light bites and lunches

In today's world, where day-to-day life is often fast-paced and busy, most of us are used to grabbing a sandwich, a packet of crisps and a chocolate bar at lunchtime. If you're avoiding gluten, you may not always be able to find gluten-free options everywhere you go. If you can, they are not necessarily the healthiest choice.

If you're serious about improving your health, it's worth taking the time and effort to have a nutritious lunch. It will set you up until your evening meal and keep you from feeling the urge to snack in the afternoon. Why not make a big batch of salad or soup then split it up into individual portions? It's easy and inexpensive – and it means that you can grab it on your way out the door!

The delicious light bites and lunch ideas in this chapter can be eaten at other times of the day, and can even work as evening meals and dinners if you increase the portion size, as desired. Mix and match – see which ones are your favourites!

From Falafel Wraps and Steak Salad to Veggie Burgers and Roast Squash with Rice, there are a range of gluten-free recipes to choose from.

SERVES : 2

Preparation time: **20 minutes**

Chilling time: **30 minutes**

Cooking time: **20 minutes**

Falafel with salad

400 g / 14 oz chickpeas (garbanzo beans),
   canned and drained

1 clove of garlic

1 tsp cumin, ground

1 tsp tahini

1 tsp harissa

2 tbsp gram flour

a handful of flatleaf parsley

1 lemon, juiced

1 litre / 35 fl. oz oil for frying

1 red onion, sliced

½ cucumber, sliced

100 g / 3 ½ oz cherry tomatoes

½ leafy cabbage, roughly chopped

extra virgin olive oil

1. Pat dry the chickpeas using kitchen paper.
   Place into a blender with the garlic, cumin,
   tahini, harissa, flour, parsley and lemon
   juice. Blend until just combined.

2. Roll into balls and set aside. If the mixture is
   too sticky, put some more gram flour on your
   hands. Refrigerate for 30 minutes to firm up
   the mixture.

3. Heat the oil in a deep fryer to 180°C / 350F.
   Carefully place the falafel into the hot oil and
   fry until golden brown. Remove and place
   onto kitchen paper to soak up any excess oil.

4. Place the chopped salad ingredients onto
   serving plates and top with the falafel.
   Drizzle with a little oil and season with
   salt and pepper.

SERVES: 2

Preparation time: **5 minutes**

Cooking time: **15 minutes**

Halibut with sautéed spinach

2 tranches halibut

60 ml / 2 fl. oz / ¼ cup olive oil

1 large leek, sliced

1 clove of garlic, finely chopped

150 g / 5 ½ oz / 2 ½ cups spinach

2 tbsp pine nuts, toasted

2 lemon wedges

1. Preheat the oven to 200°C (180°C fan) / 400F / gas 6 and heat an ovenproof griddle pan until smoking hot.

2. Brush the halibut with half the oil and season with salt and pepper. Sear one side on the griddle until nicely coloured, then turn it over and transfer the pan to the oven. Roast the halibut for 8 minutes, then transfer it to a warm plate and leave to rest.

3. While the halibut is cooking, add the rest of the oil to the sauté pan and fry the leeks for 4 minutes. Add the garlic and cook for 1 minute, then add the spinach and put on the lid. Cook for 2 minutes, then remove the lid and sauté until wilted.

4. Season the spinach with salt and pepper, then stir in the pine nuts and divide between two plates. Top with the halibut and serve with lemon wedges on the side.

SERVES: 2-4

Preparation time: **20 minutes**

Cooking time: **30 minutes**

Chilling time: **1 hour**

Sushi rolls

75 g / 3 ½ oz / ½ cup sushi rice

75 g / 3 ½ oz / ½ cup quinoa

½ tsp brown rice vinegar

½ tsp palm sugar

1 tsp gluten-free soy sauce

4 roasted sushi nori sheets

2 carrots, shredded

2 avocado, peeled and sliced

½ cucumber, cut into batons

50 g / 1 ½ oz pickled red cabbage, shredded

1. Begin by cooking the rice and quinoa as per the packet instructions. Once cooked, drain and leave to cool completely before proceeding.

2. Once cooled, add the vinegar, sugar and soy to the quinoa and rice in equal measures. Mix and taste to check seasoning.

3. Lay the nori sheets on a sushi mat or clean surface. Cover with a layer of the cooled rice and quinoa, leaving about an inch uncovered along one side, this will be where you seal the roll.

4. Place the remaining ingredients on top of the rice and quinoa placing them on the completely covered side of the roll. Take care not to overfill each of the sheets.

5. Roll from the fully covered side of the sushi roll towards the uncovered side. Gently wet the nori and complete the roll.

6. Using a sharp knife, cut into roughly one inch thick slices.

7. Serve with wasabi and dipping sauces.

MAKES : 12

Preparation time: **45 minutes**

Cooking time: **30 minutes**

Vegetable samosas

150 g / 5 oz / 1 cup white rice flour

15 g oat flour

1-2 tsp psyllium husk

1 tsp xanthan gum

1/2 tsp baking powder

60 ml / 2 fl. oz oil

60ml / 2 fl. oz / ¼ cup cold water

200 g / 7 oz potatoes, peeled and cut
   into cubes

50 g / 1 ½ oz cauliflower florets

50 g / 1 ½ oz peas

1 tsp mustard seeds

1 tsp cumin seeds

1 tsp coriander (cilantro) seeds

1 onion, diced

1 clove of garlic, minced

1 red chilli (chili), finely chopped

1 tsp garam masala

½ bunch fresh coriander (cilantro), chopped

1. For the dough, combine the first five ingredients in a bowl. Rub in the oil with your fingers until the mixture resembles breadcrumb. Add the water. Bring together into a dough.

2. Roll the dough into a ball, place into a floured bowl, then cover and leave for at least 30 minutes.

3. Add the potatoes to a pan of simmering water and cook for 10 minutes. Add the cauliflower after 5 minutes and peas for the final minute. Drain and set aside.

4. Heat the mustard, cumin and coriander seeds in a dry pan for 1 minute. Remove then grind with a pestle and mortar.

5. Add some oil and the onions to the pan. Fry for 5 minutes then add the spices, garlic, chilli and garam masala. Fry for 2 more minutes then add the vegetables to the pan. Mash them into the spices before stirring in the coriander.

6. Divide the dough into four parts and roll out to 3 cm (1 in) thickness. Using an 8 cm (3 in) pastry cutter, cut into circles then semi-circles. Wet half of the straight edge of each semi-circle and fold to form a cone. Spoon some potato mixture into the cone to fill it. Wet the rounded edge and seal the samosa. Repeat until all the dough is used.

7. Heat the oil in a deep fryer to a medium heat. Fry each samosa until golden, remove and set on kitchen paper to drain. Serve with a dipping sauce such as mint raita.

SERVES: 2

Preparation time: **15 minutes**

Cooking time: **10 minutes**

Falafel wrap

400 g / 14 oz canned chickpeas
   (garbanzo beans), drained

½ onion, diced

1 clove of garlic

1 tsp cumin, ground

1 tsp coriander (cilantro), ground

1 tsp tahini

1 tsp harissa

2 tbsp gram flour

a handful of flatleaf parsley

30 ml extra virgin olive oil

4 gluten-free wraps

1 red onion, sliced

1 lettuce, chopped

50 g / 1 ½ oz / ½ cup Cheddar cheese, grated

1 tbsp mayonnaise

1. Pat dry the chickpeas using kitchen paper. Place into a blender with the onions, garlic, cumin, coriander, tahini, harissa, flour, parsley and oil. Blend until combined but not so much that it is smooth. Season with salt and black pepper.

2. Using your hands, roll into balls and set aside. If the mixture is too sticky, put some more gram flour on your hands. Refrigerate for 30 minutes to firm up the mixture.

3. Heat the oil in a deep fryer to 180°C / 350F. Carefully place the falafel into the hot oil and fry until golden brown. Remove and place onto kitchen paper to soak up any excess oil.

4. To make the wraps, fill them with the salad, cheese, falafel and mayonnaise, then roll.

SERVES: 2

Preparation time: **10 minutes**

Marinating time: **30 minutes**

Cooking time: **15 minutes**

Tatsuta age

2 chicken thighs, skinless and boneless

2 tbsp gluten-free soy sauce

1 tbsp gluten-free sake

1 tbsp mirin

1 tsp grated ginger

1 clove garlic, minced

oil for frying

50 g / 1 ½ oz / ⅓ cup gluten-free
    panko breadcrumbs

1 lemon

1. Cut the chicken into bite-sized pieces and place
   into a mixing bowl. Add the soy, sake, mirin,
   ginger and garlic. Mix together to coat the
   chicken, cover and set aside to marinate for
   30 minutes.

2. When ready, heat the oil in a saucepan or
   fryer over a medium high heat.

3. Add the panko breadcrumbs to a clean bowl.
   Remove the chicken pieces from the marinade
   and place into the breadcrumbs. Coat each
   piece with breadcrumbs before carefully
   placing into the hot oil.

4. Fry until golden brown and place onto
   kitchen paper to collect any excess oil.

5. Serve in bowls with lemon wedges.

SERVES: 2

Preparation time: **15 minutes**

Cooking time: **20 minutes**

Chicken sweetcorn soup

1 tbsp olive oil

100 g / 3 ½ oz skinless chicken breast, diced

1 shallot, finely diced

1 clove of garlic, finely chopped

500 ml / 17 ½ fl. oz / 2 cups gluten-free chicken stock

1 sprig thyme, leaves only

2 whole sweetcorn, halved

1 lemon, juiced

salt and black pepper

1. In a deep-sided pan, heat the oil over a medium high heat. Add the chicken breast, shallot and garlic. Cook gently for 3-4 minutes, taking care not to colour the meat.

2. Pour in the chicken stock and bring to the boil and then reduce to a simmer.

3. Add the thyme, sweetcorn and lemon juice and cook for around 15 minutes until the chicken and sweetcorn is fully cooked.

4. Season with salt and black pepper to taste before pouring into serving bowls.

SERVES : 2

Preparation time: **10 minutes**

Cooking time: **10 minutes**

Crostini with mushrooms

1 tsp olive oil

1 tsp butter

100 g / 3 ½ oz Portobello mushrooms, sliced

1 tsp chopped dill, plus extra for garnish

4 slices gluten-free sourdough bread

50 g / 1 ½ oz / ½ cup gruyere cheese, sliced

a pinch of chilli (chili) flakes

sea salt and black pepper

1. In a frying pan, heat the oil and butter over a medium high heat. Add the mushrooms and chopped dill and fry until slightly browned at the edges.

2. Toast the sourdough bread while you are cooking the mushrooms.

3. Top the bread with the slices of cheese and place under the grill to melt.

4. Place the crostini onto a serving plate or board and top with the mushrooms.

5. Garnish with the chilli flakes, salt, black pepper and a sprig of dill.

SERVES : 1

Preparation time: **15 minutes**

Vegetable and beetroot hummus sandwich

1 cooked beetroot

240 g / 8 ½ oz tinned chickpeas
   (garbanzo beans), drained

25 ml extra virgin olive oil

1 tsp tahini

1 clove of garlic, crushed

1 lemon, juiced

2 slices gluten-free rye bread

1 carrot, julienned

¼ cucumber, sliced

½ red pepper, thinly sliced

50 g / 1 ½ oz spinach and watercress salad

1. To make the hummus, add the beetroot, chickpeas, oil, tahini, garlic and lemon juice to a blender or food processor. Blend on high to combine the ingredients, tasting as you go.

2. Take one slice of your bread and top with a generous amount of the beetroot hummus.

3. Top this with the remaining ingredients and top with the other slice of bread to make your sandwich.

4. Keep the remaining hummus in the fridge in an airtight container or covered bowl. It will keep for a couple of days and can be used in a variety of dishes.

SERVES: 2

Preparation time: **15 minutes**

Cooking time: **10 minutes**

steak salad

300 g / 10 ½ oz beef rump steak

2 tbsp olive oil

2 carrots

50 g / 1 ½ oz radish

100 g / 3 ½ oz cherry tomatoes

100 g / 3 ½ oz mixed leaf salad (baby leaf
   spinach, chard, pea shoots)

1 tsp wholegrain mustard

1 lemon, juiced

sea salt and black pepper

1. Remove the steak from the fridge at least
   20 minutes before cooking so that it comes
   up to room temperature.

2. Pour half the oil over the steak and coat
   the meat. Heat a griddle or heavy bottomed
   frying pan on a high heat until smoking.
   Add the steak and cook for 3-4 minutes
   on each side turning once during cooking.
   Remove to a chopping board to rest while
   you make the salad.

3. Using a mandolin, cut the carrots into ribbons
   and thinly slice the radish and place into a
   large bowl. Chop the tomatoes in half and
   add to the bowl along with the mixed leaves.

4. In a sealable jar, mix the remaining oil,
   mustard and lemon juice. Seal the jar and
   shake to combine. Season to taste then pour
   over the salad ingredients and toss to coat.

5. Season the steak and cut into thick slices.
   Add the salad to serving plates and top with
   the steak slices.

SERVES: 2

Preparation time: **15 minutes**

Cooking time: **30 minutes**

Chicken and roast vegetable salad

300 g / 10 ½ oz butternut squash, cubed

200 g / 7 oz Romano pepper,
   roughly chopped

1 tsp cumin seeds

4 cloves of garlic, lightly crushed

2 tbsp olive oil

200 g / 7 oz chicken breast, cubed

½ red onion, thickly sliced

a handful of parsley, roughly chopped

a handful of basil, roughly chopped

1 lemon, juiced

salt and black pepper

1. Preheat the oven to 200°C (180°C fan) / 400F /
    gas 6. In a large mixing bowl, combine the
    squash, peppers, cumin seeds, garlic and two
    thirds of the oil. Season with salt and pepper
    and toss to combine.

2. Transfer to a baking tray and spread evenly
    before placing into the oven to roast for
    20 minutes until tender.

3. Heat the remaining oil in a large sauté pan
    over a medium high heat. Add the chicken
    and fry for 8-10 minutes until starting to colour.

4. Add the cooked squash and peppers to the
    pan followed by the red onion and herbs and
    toss together so that the ingredients have
    combined. Squeeze over the lemon juice and
    season to taste.

5. Add to serving plates and garnish with herbs.

MAKES : 20

Preparation time: **10 minutes**

Cooking time: **10 minutes**

Fried mozzarella balls

20 mini mozzarella balls

salt and black pepper

1 tsp chilli (chili) flakes

1 egg, beaten

50 g / 1 ½ oz / ⅓ cup gluten-free
  panko breadcrumbs

oil for deep frying

1. If using a deep fryer, heat the oil up to
   180°C / 350F. If using a pan, heat the oil
   over a medium high heat.

2. Drain the mozzarella balls and dry with
   kitchen roll. Place into a bowl and season
   with salt, black pepper and the chilli flakes.

3. Place the beaten egg into a bowl. Crush the
   breadcrumbs and place them on a plate.

4. Dip the mozzarella balls in the egg and then
   roll in the breadcrumbs and set aside on a
   clean plate. Repeat until all the cheese has
   been coated.

5. Test the heat of the oil by dropping
   breadcrumb into it; it should sizzle and float.
   Cook the mozzarella balls in the oil until
   browned and crispy. You may have to do
   this in batches.

6. Serve as a lunch with a light salad or as a
   light bite with dips.

SERVES : 1

Preparation time: **10 minutes**

Cooking time: **15 minutes**

Pork and avocado open sandwich

1 tsp olive oil

1 pork loin steak

1 gluten-free ciabatta

1 clove of garlic

1 avocado

2 lemons, juiced

50 g / 1 ½ oz / ¼ cup sundried tomatoes

30 ml / 1 fl. oz gluten-free natural yogurt

a handful of chopped fresh basil and parsley

1. Heat a griddle pan over a medium-high heat. Coat the pork in the olive oil and season before cooking on the hot griddle pan. Cook for 5 to 8 minutes on each side until firm, then set aside to rest.

2. Slice the ciabatta in half and place the cut side down onto the griddle to toast. Once toasted, (it should take a 1-2 minutes), rub with the clove of garlic to flavour.

3. In a bowl, mash the avocado with half the lemon juice then season. Add the mashed avocado to the garlic rubbed sides of the toast.

4. Slice the pork and place on top of the avocado followed by the sundried tomato.

5. Mix the remaining lemon juice with the yogurt and season before spooning over the sandwich.

6. Sprinkle over the chopped herbs before serving.

SERVES: 1

Preparation time: **15 minutes**

Cooking time: **25 minutes**

Zingy summer salad

50 g / 1 ½ oz. / ¼ cup Camargue red rice

50 g / 1 ½ oz curly leaf kale

1 lemon, juice

1 tsp extra virgin olive oil

1 tsp sea salt

½ blood orange

25 g pomegranate seeds

25 g hazelnut (cob nut), roughly chopped

1 tsp sunflower seeds

1 tbsp cottage cheese

1. Add the rice to a saucepan then top up with double the volume of water. Bring to the boil and then cover and simmer for 20 minutes until cooked. Drain well and rinse.

2. Remove the tough stem from the kale and chop into bite-sized pieces. Place in a bowl with the lemon, oil and salt and squeeze the leaves to soften them. Set aside while the rice cooks.

3. Peel the orange and remove the white pith. Using a knife, remove the fleshy segment and add to the kale.

4. Add the rice to a bowl and top with the other ingredients for a refreshing and tasty salad.

SERVES: 2-4

Preparation time: **10 minutes**

Cooking time: **30 minutes**

Roasted spiced cauliflower

1 large cauliflower, florets only

1 tbsp olive oil

1 tsp tomato puree

1 red chilli, finely diced

1 tsp turmeric

1 tsp curry powder

1 tsp black mustard seeds

sea salt and freshly ground black pepper

1. Preheat the oven to 200°C (180°C fan) / 400F / gas 6.

2. Add the cauliflower to a large mixing bowl. Combine the remaining ingredients and pour over the cauliflower florets, tossing to coat the vegetables.

3. Place into the oven and roast for 25-30 minutes until slightly browned and the cauliflower has softened.

4. Serve as a lunch with some breads and dips or as a side dish to a main curry.

MAKES: 2

Preparation time: **15 minutes**

Chicken wraps

2 tortilla wraps, gluten-free

½ tsp ketchup, gluten-free

1 cooked chicken breast, sliced

a pinch of paprika

½ lemon, juiced

1 tomato, sliced into small wedges

½ yellow pepper, thinly sliced

a handful of lettuce, washed and shredded

½ cucumber, sliced

50 g / 1 ½ oz mayonnaise, gluten-free

1. Spread the ketchup over one side of each of the tortilla wraps.

2. Roll the cooked chicken breast slices in the paprika then layer them on top of the tortilla wraps, followed by the lemon juice, sliced tomatoes, yellow peppers, lettuce and cucumber.

3. Roll the tortilla wraps so that all the ingredients are firmly enveloped in the wraps, with pieces of chicken and tomato poking out the tops of the wraps.

4. Hold each wrap upright and squeeze over the mayonnaise.

5. Serve immediately with extra lemon wedges for squeezing over the wraps or keep them refrigerated in an airtight container to be eaten within two days.

Preparation time: **10 minutes**

Tuna club sandwich

3 slices gluten-free sourdough bread

100 g / 3 ½ oz tinned tuna

½ lemon, juiced

1 clove of garlic

1 tbsp extra virgin olive oil

1 red onion, sliced

30 g / 1 oz baby spinach leaves, washed

15 g / ½ oz green olive, pitted and halved

15 g / ½ oz pomegranate seeds

1. Place the bread into a toaster to toast. Remove and set aside.

2. Drain the tinned tuna and fork the chunks into a bowl. Season with salt and black pepper and mix with the lemon juice.

3. To arrange the sandwich, rub the inside edges of the bread with the garlic and a drizzle of olive oil.

4. Top the bottom slice with half of the ingredients, top with the middle slice of bread and repeat.

SERVES : 2

Preparation time: **15 minutes**

Greek salad

200 g / 7 oz mixed cherry tomatoes, sliced in half

1 red onion, roughly sliced

1 red pepper, sliced

½ cucumber, diced

50 g / 1 ½ oz / ⅓ cup black olives, sliced in half

30 ml / 1 fl. oz extra virgin olive oil

1 lemon, juiced

salt and freshly ground black pepper

100 g / 3 ½ oz / 1 cup feta cheese, roughly chopped

1. Place the tomatoes, red onion, red pepper, cucumber and black olives into a bowl and season with salt and pepper. Drizzle over half of the olive oil and the lemon juice then toss thoroughly to combine.

2. Add the ingredients to a serving bowl and top with the feta cheese. Season again and drizzle over the remaining olive oil.

3. Great as a light fresh lunch or as a side dish for barbequed meat or fish.

MAKES: 3-4

Preparation time: **10 minutes**

Cooking time: **30 minutes**

stuffed flatbreads

60 g / 2 oz / ½ cup almond flour

60 g / 2 oz / ½ cup gluten-free plain
   (all-purpose) flour

200 ml / 7 fl. oz / ¾ cup coconut milk

a pinch of salt

1 tbsp ghee

1 onion, finely chopped

1 clove of garlic, minced

a bunch of coriander (cilantro), chopped

½ tsp turmeric

½ tsp ground cumin

1 chilli (chili), deseeded and finely chopped

1. In a bowl, combine the almond flour, gluten-free plain flour, coconut milk and salt. Mix together until a batter forms.

2. In a non-stick pan, heat some of the ghee over a medium heat and ladle some of the batter into the pan. Using the back of the ladle, form into a circle, and cook until the bottom has browned. Remove and set aside. Repeat until all the batter has been used.

3. Add some more ghee or oil to the pan if needed. Add the onions and fry for around 5 minutes until soft and browned. Add the remaining ingredients and fry for 2 to 3 minutes until fragrant. Set aside to cool.

4. Preheat the oven to 180°C (160°C fan) / 350F / gas 4.

5. Take one of the half-cooked flatbreads and add enough of the onion mixture to the uncooked side to just cover it, leaving a small amount of space around the edge. Brush with a little oil or ghee and place another bread on top to create a stuffed bread. Repeat until all the breads have been used, you should have around 3 or 4 stuffed breads by the end.

6. Bake in the oven for 20 minutes until crisp and hot.

7. Serve with a dipping sauce or curry.

SERVES: 2-4

Preparation time: **10 minutes**

Cooking time: **40 minutes**

Roast squash with rice

1 butternut squash

2 tsp olive oil

salt and black pepper

200 g / 7 oz / 1 cup long grain white rice

a handful of fresh parsley, chopped

1. Preheat the oven to 200°C (180°C fan) / 400F / gas 6.

2. Peel and deseed the squash and chopped the flesh into cubes. Place into a bowl and add the olive oil and season with salt and black pepper. Toss to coat the squash with the oil.

3. Place the squash onto a baking tray, place into the oven and bake for 30 minutes until soft and tender.

4. Rinse the rice with cold water before adding to a pan. Top up with cold water, using double the amount of liquid to rice. Add a pinch of salt and bring to the boil, cover once boiling and reduce to a low simmer. Cook for around 15 minutes until the water has been absorbed, remove from the heat and leave to stand for a further 10 minutes.

5. In a large bowl, combine the cooked squash with the rice and toss together.

6. Taste to season, add the chopped parsley and a little olive oil if desired.

SERVES: 2

Preparation time: **15 minutes**

Cooking time: **20 minutes**

Chicken satay

4 skinless and boneless chicken thighs

1 tsp cumin

1 tsp coriander (cilantro), ground

½ tsp turmeric

2 red chillies (chilies), deseeded and chopped

1 clove of garlic

5 cm (2 in) piece of ginger

a bunch of coriander (cilantro)

50 g / 1 ½ oz peanut butter

1 tsp tamarind paste

2 limes, juiced

1. Cut the chicken into cubes of approximately 1 inch. Add to a large bowl and set aside.

2. In a dry pan, gently heat the cumin, coriander and turmeric until fragrant.

3. Add the toasted spices to a blender with the chillies, garlic, ginger and coriander. Blitz to a paste before adding the remaining ingredients and blending again until smooth, adding a little water if necessary.

4. Pour the peanut sauce over the chicken and mix to coat. Leave for at least 2 hours or preferably overnight to marinade.

5. To cook, heat a grill or BBQ. Place the chicken pieces onto bamboo skewers that have been soaked in water for a couple of hours. Place under the gill or onto the BBQ and cook for 20 minutes turning regularly.

6. Serve with lemon wedges and a fresh salad.

MAKES : 12

Preparation time: **30 minutes**
Cooking time: **40 minutes**

Multi-seed bread rolls

300 g / 10 ½ oz / 2 cups brown rice flour

100 g / 3 ½ oz / ²/₃ cup corn flour

50 g / 1 ½ oz / ⅓ cup chia flour

1 tsp salt

1 sachet active yeast

500 ml / 17 ½ fl. oz / 2 cups hot water

1 tbsp maple syrup

75 g / 2 ½ oz / ¾ cup flax seed

30 ml olive oil

15 g mixed seeds

1. Preheat the oven to 180˚C (160˚C fan) / 350F / gas 4 and lightly grease a 12-hole muffin tin.

2. In a large mixing bowl, combine the flours and salt and mix to combine.

3. Dissolve the yeast in the hot water as per the packet instructions adding the maple syrup. Allow it to stand until frothy for around 5 minutes. Stir in the flax seeds followed by the olive oil. Leave to stand for a further minute.

4. Pour the wet ingredients into the dry and mix to form a dough.

5. Spoon into the muffin tin and top with the mixed seeds and leave for 30 minutes to rise.

6. Bake in the oven for around 30 minutes until the rolls sound hollow when tapped.

7. Remove from the oven and allow to cool before serving.

SERVES: 2

Preparation time: **20 minutes**

Cooking time: **45 minutes**

Crispbreads with smoked salmon

100 g / 3 ½ oz / 1 cup gluten-free rolled oats

100 g / 3 ½ oz / ²/₃ cup coconut flour

150 g / 5 oz / 1 ½ cups mixed seeds
  (pumpkin, flax and sunflower)

75 g / 2 ½ oz / ¾ cup sesame seeds

2 tsp fennel seeds, cracked

50 ml / 1 ½ fl. oz olive oil

150 ml warm water

250 g / 1 ½ oz / 1 cup natural yogurt

1 lemon, juiced

40 g / 1 ½ oz cress

120 g / 4 oz smoked salmon

1. Preheat the oven to 180°C (160°C fan) / 350F / gas 4.
   You will need two baking trays and greaseproof
   paper. Cut the paper to roughly the same size as the
   baking trays.

2. Combine the oats, flour and seeds in a bowl. Pour in
   the oil and water and mix to a thick dough using
   your hands.

3. Pour half of the dough onto a sheet of baking paper.
   Top with some more greaseproof paper and roll out
   as thinly as possible so that it fills the paper. Place
   into a baking tray, paper side down and trim so
   that it fits. Repeat with the rest of the dough.

4. Score the dough with the desired cracker shape and
   bake in the oven for 45 minutes until golden brown.
   Remove and set aside to cool, break into individual
   crackers once cooled.

5. Combine the yogurt, lemon juice and cress. Season
   with salt and black pepper to taste.

6. To serve, place a spoonful of yogurt atop a cracker
   and lay some smoked salmon over each one.

7. The remaining crackers will keep for up to two weeks
   in an airtight container.

SERVES: 2

Preparation time: **2 minutes**

Cooking time: **1 hour**

Veggie burger

3 sweet potatoes, cubed

1 small cauliflower, florets only

1 tbsp olive oil

1 tsp paprika

1 tsp cumin

1 tsp chilli (chili) flakes

1 tbsp gram flour

4 spring onions (scallions), chopped

2 cooked beetroot

100 g / 3 ½ oz mayonnaise

1 lemon, juiced

50 g / 1 ½ oz baby spinach leaves

20 g pea shoots

2 gluten-free burger rolls

1. Preheat the oven to 180°C (160°C fan) / 350F / gas **4**.

2. In a bowl, combine the sweet potato, cauliflower, oil, paprika, cumin and chilli flakes. Toss to coat before adding to a baking tray. Place into the oven and bake for 30 minutes until softened.

3. Remove from the oven and place two thirds of the mixture into a blender. Blend together with the gram flour until smooth. Add to a bowl with the remaining vegetables and spring onions. Form into burger shapes, adding more flour if too sticky, and place into the fridge until needed.

4. To cook the burgers, place onto a baking tray and bake in the oven for 30 minutes until browned, carefully turning half way through cooking.

5. Make the beetroot dressing by blending together the beetroot, mayonnaise and lemon juice.

6. Make the burgers by cutting the rolls in half, adding a later of spinach followed by the burgers, dressing and pea shoots.

Main meals

Your body deserves to be nourished by a delicious, hearty main meal. Whether you prefer to eat this at midday or in the evenings, make sure you take a little time to enjoy preparing and cooking your gluten-free meal.

It is reassuring to make your own main meals too, as it means you know exactly which ingredients have been used and you can be certain that it is completely gluten-free.

The core of any nutritious dinner is a mix of protein, vegetables and starchy grains. You can easily achieve this with gluten-free foods and, if you can also make it slightly lower in fat and sugar content, that is even better! Fish, lean meats and pulses are the best way to meet your protein needs and they are easy to cook in a variety of ways.

Vegetables are a no-brainer on any diet. They are gluten-free, low in fat and sugar, and packed full of nutrients.

The starches on your dinner plate can be provided by a range of gluten-free foods, including potatoes, rice, sweet potatoes and quinoa. If you are craving pasta, treat yourself to a gluten-free version occasionally.

With inspirational recipes, such as Quinoa Tofu Bowl, Chilli Beef Tacos, Lamb Koftas with Rice and even Lasagne, there is something for everyone in this chapter.

Preparation time: **15 minutes**

Cooking time: **30 minutes**

Duck ramen bowl

1 duck breast

1 tsp Chinese five spice

1 tsp olive oil

1 tbsp honey

1 tbsp gluten-free soy sauce

500 ml / 17 ½ fl. oz / 2 cups gluten-free
   chicken stock

1 tsp sesame oil

2 shallots, finely sliced

a handful of chopped coriander (cilantro)

300 g / 10 ½ oz rice noodles, blanched

150 g / 5 oz chestnut mushrooms, sliced

1 red pepper, thinly sliced

1 green pepper, thinly sliced

2 eggs, soft boiled

1 tsp sesame seeds

2 spring onions (scallions), sliced

lettuce leaves

1. Preheat the oven to 200°C (180°C fan) / 400F /
   gas 6.

2. Score the skin side of the duck in a diamond
   shape. Rub the five-spice over the duck breast.

3. Heat the oil in an ovenproof pan over a medium
   high heat. Place the duck skin side down and cook
   for 5 minutes until browned and the fat has been
   released. Drain off any excess fat and turn over.

4. Add the honey and soy to the pan and cook
   for 1 minute before transferring to the oven.
   Roast for 8-10 minutes then remove from the
   pan to rest.

5. In a large saucepan, bring the stock to a boil and
   add the sesame oil, shallots and half the
   coriander. Reduce to a simmer, cover and cook for
   5 minutes, adding the noodles for the last minute.

6. Cook the mushrooms and peppers in the pan
   the duck was roasted in, taking care with the hot
   handle. Fry for 2-3 minutes until coloured; add a
   little oil if necessary.

7. Pour the stock and noodles into serving bowls.
   Top with slices of the duck, vegetables and the
   remaining ingredients.

SERVES: 4-6

Preparation time: **20 minutes**

Cooking time: **1 hour**

Winter vegetable stew

1 tbsp olive oil

1 large onion, sliced

1 clove of garlic, finely chopped

2 carrots, diced

1 suede, diced

500 ml / 17 ½ fl. oz / 2 cups gluten-free beef
   or vegetable stock

400 g / 14 oz chopped tomatoes

300 g / 10 ½ oz potatoes, peeled and diced

1 sprig thyme

2 bay leaves

200 g / 7 oz green (string) beans, trimmed

100 g / 3 ½ oz / ²/₃ cup garden peas

a handful of chopped flat-leaf parsley

1. In a large casserole dish, heat the oil over a medium heat. Once hot, add the onions and cook until soft and translucent, about 5 minutes.

2. Add the garlic, carrots and suede and continue to cook for a further 2-3 minutes, stirring regularly.

3. Pour in the stock and tomatoes and stir to combine. Turn up the heat and bring to the boil before reducing to a simmer. Add the potatoes and herbs, replace the lid and cook on a low heat so that it is just bubbling for 45-50 minutes.

4. Around 10 minutes before the cooking time is up, add the beans and peas. Season to taste with salt and black pepper.

5. The stew will be ready once the vegetables are soft.

6. Just before serving, check the seasoning and stir through the chopped parsley.

SERVES: 2

Preparation time: **20 minutes**

Cooking time: **15 minutes**

Quinoa tofu bowl

200 g / 7 oz. silken form tofu

60 ml / 2 fl. oz / ¼ cup gluten-free soy

15 ml / ½ fl. oz toasted sesame oil

1 tbsp honey

1 tsp chilli (chili) flakes

100 g / 3 ½ oz / 1 cup quinoa

1 tsp oil

50 g / 1 ½ oz broccoli florets

50 g / 1 ½ oz cauliflower florets

100 g / 3 ½ oz curly kale

50 g / 1 ½ oz / ½ cup flaked
   (slivered) almonds

1. Drain the tofu and wrap in kitchen paper to dry.

2. Whisk together the soy, sesame oil, honey and chilli flakes. Cut the tofu into cubes and add to the marinade and set aside for 15 minutes.

3. Add the quinoa to a saucepan and fill with double the amount of water. Bring to the boil and then simmer for 15 minutes until cooked. Drain well and set aside.

4. Heat the oil in a large frying pan or wok over a medium high heat. Add the tofu and stir-fry for 5 minutes until it is starting to colour. Add the vegetables to the pan and any remaining marinade and continue to stir-fry for another 5 minutes until the vegetables are cooked.

5. Spoon the quinoa into bowls and top with the stir-fried tofu and vegetables followed by a scattering of nuts.

SERVES: 2

Preparation time: **10 minutes**

Cooking time: **45 minutes**

Gnocchi with marinara sauce

1 tbsp olive oil

1 onion, finely chopped

200 g / 7 oz tomatoes, roughly chopped

2 cloves of garlic, crushed

a handful of chopped basil

salt and freshly ground black pepper

250 g / 1 ½ oz gluten-free gnocchi

parmesan cheese

1. Heat the oil in a large pan over a medium heat. Add the onions and cook for 5 minutes until soft.

2. Add the tomatoes and garlic and cook for a further couple of minutes before adding half of the basil and season. Cover and simmer on a low heat for around 15 minutes, until the tomatoes break down.

3. Using a hand blender, blend to a smooth sauce and taste to check seasoning. Cover and set aside until needed.

4. Bring a saucepan of salted water to the boil. Add the gnocchi and cook for a couple of minutes until they start to float.

5. Using a slotted spoon, add the gnocchi to the marinara sauce and stir through with the remaining basil and some grated parmesan cheese.

6. Serve immediately.

SERVES: 2

Preparation time: **10 minutes**

Cooking time: **25 minutes**

Vegetable rice bowl

150 g / 5 oz / 1 ½ oz basmati, wild and
   Camargue rice

200 g / 7 oz broccoli

150 g / 5 oz / 1 ½ oz chickpeas (garbanzo
   beans), tinned and drained

75 g / 2 ½ oz / 1 cup almonds

75 g/ 2 ½ oz / ²/₃ cup spring onions
   (scallions), sliced

1 lemon, juiced

1 tsp extra virgin olive oil

a bunch of coriander (cilantro), chopped

salt and black pepper

1. Add the rice to a saucepan and cover with
   roughly double the amount of water. Bring to
   the boil and then reduce to a simmer. Cover
   and cook for 20-25 minutes until cooked,
   drain well and rinse.

2. Cut the broccoli florets from the stem and
   steam over a pan of boiling water for
   5 minutes until tender but still firm.

3. In a bowl, combine the broccoli, chickpeas,
   almonds, spring onions, lemon juice, oil and
   coriander. Toss together to coat and season
   with salt and black pepper to taste.

4. Add the rice to a serving bowl and top with
   the vegetable and nut mix.

5. Serve immediately.

SERVES : 4

Preparation time: **20 minutes**

Cooking time: **2 hours**

Classic beef stew

1 tbsp olive oil

400 g / 14 oz braising steak, cubed

1 tbsp gluten-free flour

1 onion, roughly chopped

2 cloves of garlic, crushed

200 g / 7 oz chestnut mushroom, chopped

500 ml / 17 ½ fl. oz / 2 cups gluten-free beef stock

400 g / 14 oz chopped tomatoes

a small bunch of thyme

500 g / 1.1 lbs potatoes, peeled and cut into large chunks

4 carrots, sliced

1. Preheat the oven to 160°C (140°C fan) / 325F / gas 3. In a large ovenproof casserole dish, heat the oil over a medium high heat.

2. Coat the beef in the flour and add to the casserole to brown. Remove from the pan and place onto a plate and season.

3. Reduce the heat, add the onion and cook until translucent, adding more oil, if required. Once the onions are cooked, add the garlic and mushrooms. Cook for another 2 minutes.

4. Return the beef to the pan with any juices that have collected on the plate. Add the stock and chopped tomatoes to the pan, bring to the boil before adding the herbs and covering with a lid and placing in the centre of the oven.

5. After an hour, add the potatoes and carrots to the casserole and cook for a further 45 minutes or until the potatoes are soft.

6. Serve in large bowls with some gluten-free bread to soak up the juices.

SERVES: 2

Preparation time: **10 minutes**

Cooking time: **15 minutes**

Baked fish with courgette

2 x 150 g / 5 oz white fish fillets, such as cod or haddock

1 large courgette (zucchini), sliced

1 lemon, sliced

several sprigs of lemon thyme

extra virgin olive oil

salt and freshly ground black pepper

1. Preheat the oven to 220°C (200°C fan) / 425F / gas 7.

2. To prepare the fish, remove the skin and any bones using fish bone tweezers.

3. Add a drizzle of olive oil to a large piece of tin foil. Top with the sliced courgette to create a bed for the fish to sit on. Place the fish on top of the vegetables and top with the lemon and thyme. Season with salt and pepper and a further drizzle of olive oil.

4. Create a parcel by bringing the edges of the foil together. Leave some room within the parcel for the air to circulate and cook the fish.

5. Place onto a baking tray and cook in the oven for 15 minutes or until the fish is fully cooked through and easy to flake with a fork.

6. Serve with a simple side salad.

SERVES: 2

Preparation time: **15 minutes**

Cooking time: **35 minutes**

Setting time: **10 minutes**

BBQ chicken polenta pizza

700 ml / 24 fl. oz / 2 ½ cups water

salt and black pepper

100 g / 3 ½ oz / 1 cup fine polenta

1 tbsp olive oil

100 ml / 3 ½ fl. oz gluten-free BBQ sauce

100 g / 3 ½ oz leftover roast chicken

1 red onion, sliced

50 g / 1 ½ oz spring greens, chopped

1. Preheat the oven to 220°C (200°C fan) / 425F / gas 7 and grease and line two baking trays.

2. In a large saucepan, bring the water to a boil with ½ a teaspoon of salt. Once boiling, pour in the polenta and whisk. Continue to whisk until the polenta thickens, taking care as the polenta will bubble and spit. Season with salt and pepper as you stir.

3. Once the mixture has thickened, pour onto the prepared baking trays and shape into a rough pizza base shape. Leave to set for 10 minutes.

4. Brush with the olive oil and place in the preheated oven for 25 minutes until crisp and slightly coloured at the edges. Then remove and set aside.

5. Top the pizza bases with the BBQ sauce followed by the chicken, onion and greens.

6. Place back into the oven to heat through, around 10 minutes, then serve.

Preparation time: **35 minutes**

Beef tacos with salsa

2 tbsp olive oil

2 red onions, diced

2 cloves of garlic, minced

1 tsp smoked paprika

2 tsp chilli (chili) powder

500 g / 1.1 lbs beef mince

400 g / 14 oz chopped tomatoes, canned

2 avocados, lightly mashed

100 g / 3 ½ oz cherry tomatoes, diced

1 red pepper, deseeded and diced

a bunch of fresh coriander (cilantro),
    finely chopped

1 lemon, juiced

1 red chilli (chili), deseeded finely chopped

12 gluten-free taco shells

a handful of Cheddar cheese, grated

1. In a large pan, heat the oil over a medium high heat. Add half of the onion and fry for around 5 minutes until translucent. Add the garlic, frying for a minute before adding the spices and beef mince. Cook for a further 3-4 minutes until browned, before adding the tomatoes. Turn down to a simmer and cook for 30 minutes.

2. In a bowl, combine the remaining onion, avocado, tomatoes, pepper, coriander, lemon juice and chillies. Mix together with a spoon, cover and refrigerate the salsa until needed.

3. Once the chilli beef is cooked, warm up the taco shells in the oven as per the instructions.

4. To serve, place the three elements of the meal on a table together so that everyone can build their own taco. First fill with beef, then add the salsa and finish with a small sprinkling of grated cheese.

SERVES: 4-6

Preparation time: **15 minutes**

Cooking time: **45 minutes**

Baked white fish

1 tbsp olive oil

800 g / 1.7 lb white fish fillets, skinless

1 large onion, thinly sliced

2 carrots, shredded

2 lemons, juiced

a handful of fresh dill, chopped

300 ml / 10 ½ fl. oz / 1 cup soured cream

250 g / 1 ½ oz ricotta cheese

salt and white pepper

1. Preheat the oven to 180°C (160°C fan) / 350F / gas 4.

2. Heat the olive oil over a medium-high heat in a large frying pan. Season the fish with salt and pepper before browning for approximately 2-3 minutes on each side.

3. Add the fish to an ovenproof dish in a single layer. The fish should cover the base of the dish so ensure you have used something of the correct size.

4. Add the onions to the pan, turn down the heat a little, and fry for 4-5 minutes until browned, adding a little more olive oil if necessary. Add the carrots to the pan and continue to fry for a further 5 minutes.

5. Transfer the onion and carrot to a bowl, leaving as much oil in the pan as possible. Add the remaining ingredients and mix to combine them. Season with salt and pepper to taste before coating the fish with the mixture.

6. Bake the fish in the oven for 30 minutes until the top has started to brown in places. Remove from the oven and leave to stand for 5 minutes before serving.

SERVES: 4

Preparation time: **10 minutes**

Cooking time: **30 minutes**

Chinese pork with rice

400 g / 14 oz pork tenderloin

1 tsp honey

1 ½ tsp Chinese five spice

2 tsp gluten-free soy sauce

1 tsp corn flour

2 eggs

2 tsp sesame oil

250 g / 1 ½ oz rice / 1 ½ cups rice,
   cooked and cooled

150 g / 5 oz / 1 cup frozen peas, defrosted

6 spring onions (scallions), sliced

1. Preheat the oven to 180°C (160°C fan) / 350F / gas 4.

2. Trim the pork of any sinew or fat and set aside.

3. In a bowl, combine the honey, 1 teaspoon of five spice, 1 teaspoon of soy and the corn flour. Pour over the pork. Leave to marinade for an hour.

4. Place the pork into the oven and roast for 15 minutes, turning once and basting with sauce.

5. Beat the eggs with the remaining five spice and 1 teaspoon of sesame oil. In a non-stick pan, heat the remaining oil over a medium-high heat. Add the egg and cook to form a simple omelette. Remove and set aside.

6. Add the remaining oil, rice and peas to the pan and fry for 10 minutes until hot. Chop the egg into slices and add to the pan with most of the spring onions. Cook for a further few minutes and add the remaining soy sauce before removing from the heat.

7. To serve, cut the pork into slices and serve on top of the cooked rice.

8. Garnish with the remaining onions.

SERVES: 1

Preparation time: **10 minutes**

Cooking time: **5 minutes**

Grilled halloumi salad

2 tsp olive oil

½ orange, segments and juice

1 tsp white wine vinegar

1 tsp Dijon mustard

salt and black pepper

100 g / 3 ½ oz mixed leaf salad

50 g / 1 ½ oz cherry tomatoes, halved

100 g / 3 ½ oz halloumi, cut into slabs

1. Firstly, prepare the salad. Mix most of the oil, orange juice, vinegar, mustard and salt and black pepper in a jar with a tight-fitting lid. Seal and shake well to combine the ingredients, tasting to check seasoning.

2. On a serving plate, place the salad leaves, tomatoes and orange segments. Pour over the salad dressing and set aside.

3. Heat a griddle pan or BBQ to a medium-high heat. Lightly brush the halloumi with a little oil and place onto the grill. Cook for around 2-3 minutes per side until browned, remove and place on top of the salad.

4. Serve immediately whilst the halloumi is still hot as this is when it tastes best.

Preparation time: **15 minutes**

Cooking time: **20 minutes**

Lamb koftas with rice

250 g / 1.5 oz lean lamb mince

1 small onion, grated

1 clove of garlic, minced

1 red chilli (chili), finely chopped

1 tsp ground cumin

1 tsp ground coriander (cilantro)

a handful fresh mint, chopped

a handful of fresh coriander
(cilantro), chopped

100 g / 3 ½ oz / ½ cup basmati rice

1 tbsp oil

1 lemon juiced

1. In a large mixing bowl, combine the first eight ingredients. Using your hands, bring the mixture together until well mixed.

2. Using your hands, shape into balls and then flatten. Place into the refrigerator until needed, removing 10 minutes before cooking.

3. Cook the rice as per the packets instructions.

4. As the rice is cooking, heat a skillet or griddle pan over a medium-high heat. Brush each of the lamb koftas with oil and place onto the hot pan. Do not move during cooking, but flip them after around 8 minutes. It will be ready to flip once the meat has sealed and it is no longer stuck to the pan.

5. Serve the lamb koftas hot with a squeeze of lemon juice and the cooked rice and sides of your choice.

SERVES: 4

Preparation time: **30 minutes**

Cooking time: **2 hours**

Spicy beef stew with vegetables

2 tbsp olive oil

600 g / 1.3 lbs beef braising steak

1 large onions, chopped

1 clove of garlic, chopped

1 tbsp tomato puree

1 tsp chilli powder

500 ml / 17 ½ fl. oz / 2 cups gluten-free
 beef stock

1 bay leaf

2 large carrots, sliced

½ butternut squash, diced

100 g / 3 ½ oz / ⅔ cup garden peas

1 tsp cornflour (cornstarch)

1 tsp mustard powder

a handful of chopped parsley

1. Heat the oil in a large heavy bottomed pan with a lid. Add the beef and brown on all sides before removing with a slotted spoon and setting aside.

2. Add the onions to the pan with a pinch of salt and cook for 5-8 minutes until soft and translucent. Add the garlic and fry for a further minute before adding the tomato puree and chilli powder and frying for another minute. Taste and add more chilli powder, if desired.

3. Return the beef to the pan, followed by the beef stock and bay leaves. Bring to the boil and then reduce the heat to low and cover. Leave to cook for 1 hour.

4. After an hour, add the carrots, squash and peas to the pan and cook for a further 30 minutes until the vegetables are soft.

5. Mix the cornflour and mustard powder with a small amount of water to create a paste. Stir this into the casserole, remove the lid and bring back to the boil to reduce and thicken the stew.

6. Season to taste and serve with the chopped parsley.

SERVES : 2

Preparation time: **20 minutes**

Cooking time: **30 minutes**

Thai green curry

250 g / 9 oz / 1 ¼ cups Thai jasmine rice

1 tsp groundnut oil

2 tbsp Thai green curry paste

100 g / 3 ½ oz pea aubergine (eggplant)

4 kaffir lime leaves

1 stick lemongrass, bruised

1 tbsp fish sauce

1 can coconut milk

300 g / 10 ½ oz chicken thighs,
   skinless and boneless

a sprig of basil

1 fresh red chilli (chili) sliced

1. In a saucepan, cook the rice as per the packet instructions and keep warm while you prepare the curry.

2. Heat the oil in a wok over a medium-high heat. Add the curry paste and fry for 1-2 minutes until fragrant. Add the aubergine, lime leaves, lemongrass and fish sauce continuing to fry for a further 2 minutes. If the ingredients are looking a little dry, add a splash of the coconut milk.

3. Pour in the coconut milk before adding the sliced chicken. Bring to the boil and then reduce to a simmer for 12-15 minutes, until the meat is cooked.

4. Serve in a bowl and garnish with the basil and chilli, with the rice on the side.

SERVES: 2

Preparation time: **30 minutes**

Cooking time: **10 minutes**

Healthy kale and quinoa salad

1 clove of garlic, minced

1 tbsp Dijon mustard

60 ml / 2 fl. oz / ¼ cup of balsamic vinegar

1 lemon, juiced

1 tbsp raw organic honey

100 ml / 3 fl. oz / ½ cup extra virgin olive oil

200 g / 7 oz kale

50 g / 1 ½ oz / ¼ cup quinoa,
    cooked and drained

30 g sundried tomatoes

1 tbsp white wine vinegar

2 eggs

1. Make the vinaigrette by combining the first 6 ingredients in a jar before sealing and shaking well. Season to taste, adding further honey, if it requires sweetening. Leave to combine for 30 minutes before using.

2. To prepare the kale, remove the tough stems and cut into bite-sized pieces. Place into a bowl and add some salt and squeeze the leaves to soften them. Rinse well before using.

3. To make the salad, combine the raw kale leaves with the quinoa and tomatoes before pouring over some dressing. Toss to combine and coat the ingredients.

4. To poach the eggs, bring a small saucepan of water with the white wine vinegar to just boiling. Crack each egg into a ramekin before carefully dropping into the water. Leave to cook for approximately 4-5 minutes. Remove with a slotted spoon and place onto kitchen paper to soak up any further water.

5. Place the poached egg on top of the salad and serve.

SERVES : 2-4

Preparation time: **20 minutes**

Marinating time: **4 hours or overnight**

Cooking time: **45 minutes**

Chicken tikka masala

500 g / 1.1 lbs / 2 ½ cups natural yogurt

1 tsp hot paprika

1 tsp chilli (chili) powder

½ tsp turmeric

2 clove of garlic, minced

3 lemons

500 g / 1.1 lbs chicken breast, cubed

1 tbsp oil

2 onions, sliced

2.5 cm (1 in) piece of fresh ginger, grated

2 red chillies (chilies), finely chopped

1 tsp mustard seeds

1 tsp garam masala

400 g / 14 oz canned chopped tomatoes

a bunch of fresh coriander (cilantro), chopped

150 g / 5 oz basmati rice

1. In a bowl, combine 400 g of yogurt, the paprika, chilli powder, turmeric, half the garlic and the juice of 1 lemon. Mix to form a smooth marinade, then add the chicken pieces. Season then cover and leave to marinade for at least 4 hours.

2. Heat the oil in a pan with a lid. Add the onions and cook for 5-8 minutes until browned. Add the ginger, garlic, chilli, mustard seeds and garam masala. Fry for 3 minutes until fragrant then add the tomatoes. Bring to the boil, then reduce to a simmer, cover and cook for 30 minutes.

3. Preheat the oven to 200°C (180°C fan) / 400F / gas 6.

4. Cook the rice as per the packet instructions and keep warm.

5. Place the marinated chicken onto a baking tray and cook into the oven for 12-15 minutes. Remove and drain off any liquid.

6. Stir in the remaining yogurt to the sauce, before adding the chicken pieces to warm through.

7. Serve with the rice and garnish with chopped coriander and some gluten-free bread, if desired.

SERVES: 6-8

Preparation time: **20 minutes**

Cooking time: **1 hour 30 minutes**

Lasagne

1 tsp olive oil

80 g / 3 oz cubetti di pancetta

1 large onion, diced

2 cloves of garlic, finely chopped

500 g / 1.1 lbs lean beef mince

1 tsp tomato puree

400 g / 14 oz can chopped tomatoes

1 gluten-free beef stock cube

a handful of fresh basil, chopped

1 litre / 35 fl. oz semi-skimmed milk

30 g unsalted butter

30 g gluten-free plain (all-purpose) flour

30 g corn flour

75 g / 2 ½ oz Parmesan cheese

250 g / 1 ½ oz gluten-free lasagne sheets

200 g / 7 oz / 2 cups mozzarella, grated

125 g / 4 ½ oz buffalo mozzarella, sliced

1. Preheat the oven to 180°C (160°C fan) / 350F / gas 4.

2. In a large saucepan, heat the olive oil over a medium heat. Add the pancetta and fry for 5 minutes until starting to brown. Add the onions and cook for a further 5 minutes until softened. Add the garlic and fry for a further minute.

3. Add the beef and tomato puree to the pan and fry until the meat has browned. Pour in the tomatoes and crumble the stock cube into the pan. Reduce to a simmer then cover and cook for 30 minutes, adding the basil for the last 10 minutes.

4. Make the white sauce by combining the milk, butter, flour and corn flour in a saucepan. Gently heat, whisking continuously until thickened. Grate in the parmesan cheese and season well.

5. To make the lasagne, spoon a layer of the beef sauce into a rectangular ovenproof dish. Top with a layer of pasta then a later of white sauce. Repeat until all the sauce is gone, finishing with a layer of white sauce. Top with the grated and sliced cheese.

6. Bake in the oven for 45 minutes until the top has browned and the pasta has softened.

7. Serve with a crisp salad.

SERVES: 1

Preparation time: **5 minutes**

Cooking time: **20 minutes**

pasta with broccoli and prawns

180 g / 6 ½ oz gluten-free fusilli

100 g / 3 ½ oz / ¾ cup broccoli

1 tsp olive oil

100 g / 3 ½ oz raw king prawns

1 tsp chilli (chili) flakes

2 lemons

several sprigs of dill

1. Fill a saucepan with water and a pinch of salt and bring to the boil. Add the pasta and cook for 15-20 minutes until softened but still with a little bite.

2. While the pasta is cooking, chop the broccoli florets from the main stem. Steam for around 5 minutes using a vegetable steamer until tender.

3. At the same time, heat the oil in a small frying pan. Once hot, add the prawns and cook until pink and firm to the touch. Add the chilli flakes and the juice from one of the lemons and cook for a further minute then set aside.

4. Drain the pasta and top with the prawns and broccoli.

5. Garnish with sprigs of dill and quarters of lemon to squeeze over the top.

SERVES: 2

Preparation time: **20 minutes**

Cooking time: **30 minutes**

Vegetable stew with rice

150 g / 5 oz / 1 ½ cups brown basmati
  and wild rice

1 tbsp olive oil

1 green pepper, sliced

1 red pepper, sliced

1 clove of garlic, crushed

1 tsp paprika

100 g / 3 ½ oz / 1 cup flageolet beans

225 g / 8 oz chopped tomatoes

salt and black pepper

a handful of chopped parsley

1. Soak the rice in water for 20 minutes and
   then drain. Add to a saucepan and top up
   with twice the amount of water. Bring to
   the boil and then reduce to a simmer until
   cooked, around 20-25 minutes.

2. Heat the oil in a sauté pan over a medium
   high heat. Add the peppers and cook until
   softened, around 5 minutes.

3. Add the garlic and paprika and fry for a
   further minute before adding the beans
   and chopped tomatoes. Bring to the boil and
   then reduce to a simmer and cover with a lid.

4. Once the rice has cooked, rinse the grains
   through a sieve using boiling water before
   adding to serving plates.

5. Season the stew with salt and pepper to taste
   and spoon on top of the cooked rice. Top with
   the chopped parsley to garnish.

SERVES: 4

Preparation time: **15 minutes**

Proving time: **1 hour**

Cooking time: **15 minutes**

Cherry tomato and cheese pizza

1 x 7 g sachet of dried yeast

1 tbsp caster (superfine) sugar

400 g / 14 oz / 2 ⅔ cups gluten-free bread flour

1 tsp xanthan gum

1 large free-range egg, beaten

200 ml / 7 fl. oz / 3/4 cup semi-skimmed milk

olive oil

½ tsp bicarbonate of soda

2 tsp white wine vinegar

250 g / 1 ½ oz passata

1 clove of garlic, minced

150 g / 5 oz / 1 ½ cups Cheddar cheese, grated

100 g / 3 ½ oz cherry tomatoes, halved

50 g / 1 ½ oz Pecorino, sliced

fresh basil leaves

1. Preheat the oven to 220°C (200°C fan) / 425F / gas 7.

2. In a bowl, mix the yeast and sugar with 50 ml of lukewarm water. Cover and set aside to allow the yeast to activate; it should start to foam.

3. In a large mixing bowl, combine the flour, xanthan gum and a pinch of salt. Mix the egg, milk and olive oil in a jug. Create a well in the centre of the dry ingredients before pouring in the milk and yeast mixtures. Bring together until a dough forms.

4. Combine the bicarbonate of soda and vinegar, quickly add to the dough and knead. Place the dough into a lightly oiled bowl, cover and leave in a warm place for an hour or until doubled in size.

5. Divide the dough into four and roll out to roughly 2 mm thickness. Combine the passata and garlic and then ladle a quarter onto each pizza base, spread out leaving some space around the edge. Top with the grated cheese and the cherry tomatoes.

6. Place each pizza onto a baking tray or pizza tray and bake for 10-12 minutes until crisp and the cheese has browned. Remove and top with the Pecorino slices and fresh basil leaves.

SERVES: 4

Preparation time: **15 minutes**

Cooking time: **45 minutes**

Baked chicken with new potatoes

4 chicken thighs

1 tsp honey

1 tsp olive oil

2 lemons, juiced

1 clove of garlic, minced

1 tsp Dijon mustard

500 g / 1.1 lbs new potatoes

10 g fresh dill, chopped

10 g butter

10 g fresh parsley, chopped

1. Preheat the oven to 180°C (160°C fan) / 350F / gas 4.

2. Trim the chicken thighs of any excess skin and place into a mixing bowl. Combine the honey, oil, half the lemon juice, garlic and mustard. Pour over the chicken, season with salt and black pepper, then set aside for at least an hour to marinade.

3. Place the chicken onto a baking tray and place in the hot oven for 45 minutes.

4. Bring a large pan of salted water to boil. Add the potatoes and cook for 30 minutes until softened. Drain and return to the pan with the remaining lemon juice, dill and butter. Shake gently to coat the potatoes.

5. To serve, place the potatoes in a large serving bowl and top with the baked chicken.

6. Garnish with chopped parsley and serve.

Desserts

Before you try it out, preparing a gluten-free dessert can sometimes seem a little daunting. If you are used to cakes, crumbles and pies, it may be hard to think of a dessert that doesn't contain wheat flour.

However, you can easily substitute wheat flour for gluten-free flour in your recipes. Experiment with the various types of gluten-free flour available; some will work better than others depending on the dessert. Some sweet treats, such as brownies, actually work better with no flour at all, as they become richer and stickier (and tastier).

There are a wide range of new ingredients to try and experiment with in desserts. For example, rice, tapioca and potato flour can add texture to baking. You can also make delicious gluten-free cheesecakes and custard tarts by swapping out the wheat in the crust or base.

This chapter contains some delicious recipes that you might not believe are in fact gluten-free! From Chocolate Ramekin Puddings and Raspberry Cheesecake Brownies to Lemon Tart with Blueberries and Cheesecake with Summer Berries, there are so many delicious, refreshing dessert recipes to try out.

MAKES: 4

Preparation time: **15 minutes**

Cooking time: **15 minutes**

Chocolate ramekin pudding

100 g / 3 ½ oz / ⅔ cup dark chocolate

200 ml / 7 fl. oz / ¾ cup double
  (heavy) cream

75 g / 2 ½ oz / ⅓ cup caster
  (superfine) sugar

2 tbsp gluten-free plain (all-purpose) flour

1 tsp gluten-free baking powder

butter and cocoa powder for
  preparing ramekins

1. Preheat the oven to 200°C (180°C fan) / 400F /
   gas 6 and lightly grease four ramekins and
   dust with cocoa powder.

2. Break the chocolate into a heatproof bowl.

3. In a saucepan, gently heat the cream until
   just starting to bubble. Pour over the
   chocolate and stir to melt completely.

4. Mix the sugar, flour and baking powder into
   the chocolate and cream mixture until
   just combined.

5. Pour into the prepared ramekins and place
   onto a baking tray.

6. Cook in the oven for 15 minutes until risen
   and still slightly moist.

7. Remove and eat hot or leave to cool
   if preferred.

8. Delicious topped with whipped cream
   or ice cream.

SERVES: 8

Preparation time: **1 hour**

Cooking time: **45 minutes**

Chilling time: **4 hours or overnight**

Orange mousse cake

3 x 12 g sachet of gelatine powder

325 g caster (superfine) sugar

800 ml freshly squeeze orange juice

175 g butter

2 large eggs

175 g polenta

50 g / 1 ½ oz ground almonds

1 tsp gluten-free baking powder

75 ml natural yogurt

1 tsp orange blossom water

500 ml / 17 ½ fl. oz / 2 cups double (heavy) cream, whisked

1. Whisk one sachet of gelatine powder, 150 ml boiling water and 50 g sugar together until dissolved. Pour in 350 ml of orange juice and stir well. Set aside to cool.

2. Line a 23 cm (9 in) tin with cling film. Pour in the orange mixture. Put in the fridge for 2 hours until set.

3. Preheat the oven to 160°C (140°C fan) / 325F / gas 3 and lightly grease and line a 23cm cake tin.

4. Whisk together the butter and 175 g sugar. Add the eggs, polenta, almonds, baking powder, yogurt and orange blossom water and mix until combined.

5. Pour into the prepared tin and bake in the oven for 30 minutes or until a skewer inserted into the centre of the cake comes out clean. Remove from the oven to cool.

6. In a pan, heat the remaining orange juice, gelatine powder and sugar. Stir until dissolved then place in the fridge for 30 minutes. Once cooled, add half the mixture to the whisked cream to form a mousse. Put the rest in the fridge.

7. To assemble the cake, place a domed layer of orange mousse into the sponge centre. Top this with the first jelly layer, which should be set. Add the remaining mousse so that the cake is completely covered. Place on a wire rack over a tray and pour over the partly set orange glaze mixture. Smooth with a spatula, place on a plate and refrigerate until set.

SERVES: 8

Preparation time: **5 minutes**

Cooking time: **15 minutes**

Freezing time: **4 hours or overnight**

Chocolate ice cream

500ml / 17 ½ fl. oz / 2 cups double
   (heavy) cream

250ml / 9 fl. oz / 1 cup full-fat milk

50 g / 1 ½ oz / ½ cup cocoa powder

300 g / 10 ½ oz / 2 cups plain
   chocolate chips

6 egg yolks

100 g / 3 ½ oz / ½ cup sugar

1. Heat the cream and milk in a large saucepan over a medium heat. Bring it up to not quite a simmer but just steaming.

2. Remove from the heat and whisk in the cocoa powder and half the chocolate chips until completely smooth.

3. In a separate bowl, whisk the egg yolks and sugar until light and fluffy. Gradually add the chocolate mixture a ladleful at a time, whisking continuously.

4. Return the mixture to your saucepan and gently bring back up to a simmer, whisking continuously, ensuring that it doesn't boil.

5. Strain into a large bowl to remove any bits of egg that may have cooked. Place in the refrigerator to chill for a few hours.

6. Pour the ice cream mixture into an ice cream maker and process as per the manufacturer's guidelines. Once finished, place into the freezer for at least 4 hours or overnight to completely set.

7. Once frozen, top with the remaining chocolate chips and serve.

SERVES: 2

Preparation time: **1 hour 10 minutes**

Chia and berry smoothie pudding

350ml / 12 fl. oz / 1 cup of coconut milk

2 tsp of coconut nectar

½ cup chia seeds

1 tsp vanilla extract

300 g / 10 ½ oz / 2 cups frozen mixed berries

200 g / 7 oz / 1 cup natural yogurt

1 banana

fresh berries and granola to garnish

a sprig of mint

1. Combine the chia seeds, coconut milk, coconut nectar and vanilla extract in a bowl. Cover and refrigerate for at least an hour until the seeds have absorbed the liquid and expanded.

2. Place the frozen berries, yogurt and banana into a high-powered blender. Blend for a couple of minutes until smooth.

3. Spoon the chia mixture into the bottom of serving glasses or bowls. Top with the berry smoothie mixture and place into the refrigerator until needed.

4. Before serving top the puddings with some fresh berries, granola and a sprig of mint.

Preparation time: **20 minutes**

Cooking time: **30 minutes**

Raspberry cheesecake brownies

225 g / 8 oz / 1 ½ cups dark chocolate

225 g / 8 oz / 1 cup butter

3 tsp vanilla extract

275 g / 9 ½ oz / 1 ¼ cups caster (superfine) sugar

4 large eggs

150 g / 5 oz / 1 ½ cups ground almonds

225 g / 8 oz / 1 cup cream cheese

100 g / 3 ½ oz / ⅔ cup fresh raspberries

a sprig of mint, to garnish

1. Preheat the oven to 180°C (160°C fan) / 350F / gas 4 and grease and line an 8-inch square tin.

2. In a large, heavy-bottomed saucepan, gently melt the chocolate and butter. Once melted, remove from the heat and stir in 2 teaspoons of the vanilla extract and 200 g of the caster sugar until dissolved.

3. Beat three of the eggs and add to the chocolate mixture once it has cooled sufficiently, followed by the ground almonds. Once combined, pour into the baking tin and set aside.

4. In a large mixing bowl, combine the remaining vanilla, sugar, egg and cream cheese and mix until smooth. Chop 80 g of the raspberries into halves and stir into the mixture.

5. Pour the raspberry mixture on top of the chocolate and bake in the oven for 30 minutes until the top has set but the rest is still gooey. Remove from the oven and, once cooled, cut into 16 squares.

6. Serve with a garnish of the remaining fresh raspberries and a sprig of mint.

SERVES: 8

Preparation time: **10 minutes**

Cooking time: **15 minutes**

Freezing time: **4 hours or overnight**

Strawberry ice cream

200 g / 7 oz / ¾ cup caster (superfine) sugar

1 tsp vanilla extract

500 g / 1.1 lbs fresh strawberries, chopped

500 ml / 17 ½ fl. oz / 2 cups whole milk

500 ml / 17 ½ fl. oz / 2 cups double (heavy) cream

1. In a saucepan, gently heat the caster sugar, vanilla extract and 400 g of the strawberries. Keep stirring until the sugar has melted and the strawberries are beginning to break down. Remove from the heat to cool.

2. Once cooled, pour into a blender and blend to a puree.

3. In a bowl, mix the strawberry puree with the cream and milk until combined and add the remaining strawberry pieces.

4. Pour the mixture into an ice cream maker and process as per the manufacturer's instructions.

5. Place into the freezer for at least 4 hours or preferably overnight.

MAKES: 12

Preparation time: **30 minutes**

Chilling time: **15 minutes**

Cooking time: **20 minutes**

Lemon tart with blueberries

175 g / 6 oz. / 1 ¼ cups gluten-free plain (all-purpose) flour

½ tsp xanthan gum

100 g / 3 ½ oz / ½ cup unsalted butter, cold cut into cubes

30 g / 1 oz. / ¼ cup icing (confectioner's) sugar

5 free-range eggs

100 ml / 3 ½ fl. oz / ½ cup double (heavy) cream

150 g / 5 oz / 1 ½ cups caster (superfine) sugar

3 lemons, juice and zest

100 g / 3 ½ oz blueberries

1. To make the pastry, place the flour, xanthan gum, butter and icing sugar into a food processor and pulse until it forms a breadcrumb-like consistency.

2. Add one egg to the mixture and 1 tablespoon of cold water. Mix until a dough forms. Turn out onto a floured surface and knead to bring the dough together. Roll into a ball, wrap in cling film and chill in the fridge for 15 minutes.

3. Preheat the oven to 200°C (180°C fan) / 400F / gas 6 and grease and line 12 7.5 cm fluted tart tins.

4. Roll out the pasty to a thickness of about 5 mm and, using a 10 cm (4 in) round cutter, cut out the tart bases. Place into the tins, add a layer of baking parchment and a few baking beans.

5. Blind bake the cases for 7-8 minutes, remove the parchment and beans, then bake for a further 3-4 minutes. Remove from the oven and turn the oven heat down to 180°C (160°C fan) / 350F / gas 4.

6. In a bowl, add the remaining eggs, cream, sugar and lemon. Whisk until combined and pour into the prepared and cooled tart bases.

7. Bake in the oven for 7 minutes until set. Remove to cool and decorate with the blueberries.

SERVES: 8

Preparation time: **10 minutes**

Cooking time: **30 minutes**

Chocolate and vanilla cake

FOR THE CAKE

250 g / 1 ½ oz / 1 ¼ cups unsalted
   butter, softened

250 g / 1 ½ oz / 1 ¼ cups caster (superfine) sugar

3 large eggs

2 tsp vanilla extract

250 g / 1 ½ oz / 1 ²/₃ cups gluten-free plain
   (all-purpose) flour

1 tsp gluten-free baking powder

FOR THE ICING

225 g / 8 oz / 1 ½ cups dark chocolate

200 g / 7 oz / 2 cups icing (confectioner's) sugar

1 tbsp granulated sugar

1. Preheat the oven to 190°C (170°C fan) / 375F / gas 5 and grease and line an 8" round cake tin.

2. Using a cake mixer, cream together the butter and sugar until light and fluffy. Add the eggs one at a time until combined, followed by the vanilla extract.

3. Fold in the flour and baking powder until you have a smooth batter. If it is a little dry, add a splash of milk (although the batter should be quite dense).

4. Pour into the prepared tin and bake in the oven for 20-25 minutes until a skewer inserted into the cake comes out clean. Remove from the oven and allow to cool slightly in the tin before transferring to a wire rack to cool completely.

5. To prepare the icing, melt the dark chocolate in a glass bowl set over a saucepan of simmering water, ensuring that the water does not touch the bowl.

6. Once melted, take the chocolate off the heat and mix in the icing sugar.

7. Immediately drizzle the melted chocolate over the cake so that it drizzles down the sides.

8. Sprinkle over some granulated sugar as decoration then leave to cool so that the chocolate sets.

Preparation time: **10 minutes**

Passion fruit dessert

4 passion fruit, ripe

200 ml / 7 fl. oz / ¾ cup double (heavy) cream

1 lemon, zest only

½ pomegranate, seeds only

1. Cut the ripe passion fruit in half. You can tell when they are ripe, as the flesh will be slightly wrinkled. Spoon out a small amount of the flesh for garnish.

2. In a mixing bowl, whip the cream until thick. Fold through the lemon zest and add to a piping bag with a star nozzle.

3. Pipe the cream on top of the halved passion fruit.

4. Garnish with the reserved passion fruit and pomegranate seeds.

S E R V E S : 8-10

Preparation time: **45 minutes**

Cooking time: **1 hour**

Chilling time: **at least 4 hours**

Cheesecake with summer berries

100 g / 3 ½ oz / ¾ cup pecans

200 g / 7 oz / Medjool dates

100 g / 3 ½ oz almond butter

750 g / 1 lb 6 oz cream cheese

1 tsp vanilla extract

1 lemon, juice and zest

100 g / 3 ½ oz / ¹⁄₃ cup fruit syrup

4 eggs

2 tbsp plain gluten-free flour

½ tsp xanthan gum

300 ml / 10 fl. oz / 1 ¼ cup organic soured cream

mixed summer berries

icing (confectioner's) sugar

1. Preheat the oven to 160°C (140°C fan) / 325F / gas 3 and grease and line the base of a 20 cm (8 in) springform cake tin.

2. In a food processor, blend together the pecans, dates and almond butter until well combined. Press firmly into the base of the tin and the sides. Chill in the fridge for 30 minutes.

3. In a large bowl, gently beat together the cheese, vanilla, lemon and syrup until just combined. Add the flour, xanthan gum and eggs, one at a time, and mix gently before folding in the soured cream.

4. Pour into the prepared base and bake in the oven for 1 hour or until set in the middle. Remove from the oven and leave to cool inside the cake tin for 2 hours before placing into the fridge for a further 4 hours or overnight.

5. To serve, carefully remove from the cake tin and place on a serving plate.

6. Top with fresh fruit and dust with icing sugar to finish.

Treats

If you are going gluten-free to try to lose weight, you will need to keep snacks and treats to a minimum. However, if you are leading a gluten-free lifestyle due to dietary requirements or allergies, the following snacks are perfect for banishing those hunger pangs mid-morning or mid-afternoon. Once you change your diet to include more slow-burning, nutrient-rich foods, you should start to feel fuller for longer. Having said this, a snack or treat can still be a great way to keep your energy levels up throughout the day.

There are lots of gluten-free options for healthy snacks. A handful of nuts, berries or raisins can be a delicious pick-me-up and they are very easy to keep in your handbag or desk drawer. If you feel the need for a sweet treat, you could use fromage frais as a dip for sliced apples or strawberries.

The following chapter will help you create delicious, gluten-free snacks. From easy-to-make Banana Pops and Madeleines to tasty Sweet Cinnamon Rolls, there are many recipes to keep your gluten-free diet varied and interesting.

SERVES : 4

Preparation time: **10 minutes**

Cooking time: **5 hours**

Melon sorbet with blueberries

2 charantais melons, halved

1 tbsp Midori (melon liqueur)

1 egg white, lightly beaten

150 g / 5 ½ oz / 1 cup blueberries

4 mint sprigs

1. Scoop out and discard the seeds of the melons, then use a spoon to scrape out the flesh. Roughly chop the flesh and put it in a freezer bag, then freeze for 4 hours or until solid.

2. Transfer the frozen melon to a food processor and process for 2 minutes. Add the Midori and egg white and process to a smooth sorbet.

3. Spoon the sorbet into a plastic tub with a lid and freeze for 1 hour.

4. Scoop the sorbet into four glass dessert dishes and serve with the blueberries and mint.

MAKES: 12

Preparation time: **10 minutes**

Cooking time: **15 minutes**

Peanut butter and oatmeal cookies

200 g / 7 oz / ¾ cup chunky peanut butter

150 g / 5 oz / ¾ cup light brown sugar

1 egg

1 tsp vanilla extract

50 g / 1 ½ oz / ½ cup rolled oats

20 g dried cranberries

1. Preheat the oven to 200°C (180°C fan) / 400F / gas 6 and line a baking tray with greaseproof paper.

2. In a bowl, mix together the almond butter, sugar, egg and vanilla extract. Once combined stir in the oats and cranberries until you have a stiff dough.

3. Using your hand, roll pieces of the dough into a ball roughly the size of a golf ball. Flatten each one slightly and place onto the baking tray.

4. Place into the oven and bake for 10 minutes until lightly golden. Remove to cool on the tray for 5 minutes and then a wire rack to cool completely.

MAKES: 8

Preparation time: **10 minutes**

Freezing time: **3 hours**

Banana pops

4 bananas

100 g / 3 ½ oz / ⅔ cup gluten-free chocolate

50 g / 1 ½ oz / ½ cup desiccated coconut

50 g / 1 ½ oz / ½ cup hazelnuts
(cob nuts), chopped

30 g gluten-free cake sprinkles

1. Peel the bananas and chop each one in half.
   Insert a lolly stick into each half.

2. Place onto a baking tray and cover with cling
   film. Place in the freezer for at least three
   hours or until completely frozen.

3. Once the bananas are frozen, remove them
   from the freezer.

4. In a bain-marie, melt the chocolate, stirring
   regularly. Take care that the boiling water
   does not touch the bottom of the bowl
   suspended over the water.

5. Pour the melted chocolate into a bowl. Roll
   the frozen bananas in the melted chocolate
   to coat them, then roll in a topping of your
   choice, such as desiccated coconut, hazelnuts
   or cake sprinkles.

6. Eat immediately or place onto greaseproof
   paper and cover before re-freezing.

MAKES: 6

Preparation time: **10 minutes**

Freezing time: **at least 3 hours**

Summer berry sorbet lollies

500 g / 1.1 lbs / 3 ⅓ cups fresh
   summer berries

1 orange, juiced

1 lemon, juiced

2 egg whites

100 g / 3 ½ oz / ½ cup caster
   (superfine) sugar

1. Add the berries, orange juice and lemon juice into a blender and blend to a smooth puree. Strain through a sieve into a sealable container.

2. Place into the freezer and remove every 30 minutes to stir until a slushy and slightly icy texture is achieved.

3. In a stand mixer, whisk the egg whites until stiff and add the sugar, continuing to whisk until firm and glossy.

4. Fold the egg whites into the sorbet base until completely combined.

5. Pour into moulds and insert a lolly stick in each one. Garnish with additional berries, if desired.

6. Place back into the freezer until completely set.

MAKES : 12

Preparation time: **30 minutes**

Cooking time: **10 minutes**

Madeleines

butter, for greasing

1 tsp icing (confectioner's) sugar

2 large eggs

100 g / 3 ½ oz / ½ cup golden caster
    (superfine) sugar

100 g / 3 ½ oz / ⅔ cup gluten-free plain
    (all-purpose) flour

1 tsp xanthan gum

1 lemon, juice and zest

1 tsp gluten-free baking powder

100 g / 3 ½ oz / ½ cup butter

1. Preheat the oven to 200˚C (180˚C fan) / 400F /
   gas 6. Lightly grease a madeleine tray and
   dust with a little icing sugar.

2. In a large mixing bowl, whisk together
   the eggs and sugar until light and fluffy.
   Gradually add the remaining ingredients,
   whisking all the time.

3. Leave the mixture to stand for around 15 to
   20 minutes before gently spooning or pouring
   into the madeleine moulds in the tray.

4. Bake in the centre of the oven for 10 minutes
   until slightly risen and cooked through.
   Place onto a wire rack to cool completely
   and enjoy fresh with a cup of tea or coffee.

MAKES: 16

Preparation time: **15 minutes**

Chilling time: **30 minutes**

Cooking time: **20 minutes**

Sweet cinnamon rolls

150 g / 5 oz gluten-free puff pastry

75 g / 2 ½ oz / ⅓ cup unsalted
butter, softened

75 g / 2 ½ oz / ½ cup brown sugar, plus more
for dusting

3 tsp ground cinnamon

1 egg, beaten

a splash of milk

1. Preheat the oven to 180°C (160°C fan) / 350F /
   gas 4.
2. Roll out the puff pastry to form a rectangle
   approximately 30 x 40 cm (12 x 16 in).
3. Mix together the butter, sugar and cinnamon
   until well combined. Spread the mixture over
   the prepared pastry until completely covered.
4. Roll the pastry along the short edge into a
   sausage. Chill in the fridge for 15 minutes
   before cutting with a sharp knife into slices.
   Lay the slices in a baking tray (use more than
   one tray, if needed), packing them tightly.
   Chill in the fridge for a further 15 minutes.
5. Whisk together the egg with a small amount
   of milk. Brush the cinnamon rolls with the
   egg mixture, sprinkle with some more sugar
   before baking for around 20 minutes until
   golden brown.

Meal plans and diary

When starting a new diet, it's important to have a plan. Otherwise you'll have a day – probably fairly early on – where you're pressed for time and don't have a gluten-free menu planned or ingredients bought. It's at times like these that you're likely to reach for whatever is available… which may contain gluten.

Before you start, sit down and think about how you want to tackle going gluten-free. If you've been diagnosed with coeliac disease, follow your doctor's or dietitian's advice. If not, decide whether you want to go cold turkey or cut gluten out of your diet more gradually. Maybe you could start by eating one gluten-free meal a day for the first week, then two in the second and so on. Also, jot down some targets for exercise. It may seem like a lot to think about but, once you get into the swing of things, it becomes second nature.

Have a go

In this chapter, you can plan and track your progress for four weeks. You can mix and match the recipes in this book or find new ones. What's included here is only the tip of the iceberg as far as delicious gluten-free food is concerned!

Once you've got your plan in place and your shopping list written, make sure you keep a record of everything you eat and drink. In addition, jot down how you feel and any digestive symptoms that you may have. If you're still having symptoms after going fully gluten-free, it may be something else that is causing them.

Your food diary can help you and your GP look for a pattern and find a solution.

Week 1

	Breakfast	Lunch	Dinner	Snacks
Monday				
Tuesday				
Wednesday				
Thursday				
Friday				
Saturday				
Sunday				

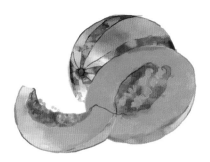

New foods that I've tried

Exercise log

Starting and finishing weight

How I feel

Week 2

	Breakfast	Lunch	Dinner	Snacks
Monday				
Tuesday				
Wednesday				
Thursday				
Friday				
Saturday				
Sunday				

New foods that I've tried

Exercise log

Starting and finishing weight

How I feel

Week 3

	Breakfast	Lunch	Dinner	Snacks
Monday				
Tuesday				
Wednesday				
Thursday				
Friday				
Saturday				
Sunday				

New foods that I've tried

Exercise log

Starting and finishing weight

How I feel

Week 4

	Breakfast	Lunch	Dinner	Snacks
Monday				
Tuesday				
Wednesday				
Thursday				
Friday				
Saturday				
Sunday				

New foods that I've tried

Exercise log

Starting and finishing weight

How I feel

A gluten-free kitchen

It's easiest to stick to a gluten-free diet if your kitchen cupboards aren't full of wheat-based foods. Before you start, have a clear-out and get rid of the things you're no longer going to eat. Stocking your cupboards with a range of gluten-free ingredients and foods is the first step towards a new, healthier you.

Here are some of the basic ingredients that no gluten-free kitchen should be without:

GRAINS AND PULSES

buckwheat

brown rice

chickpeas (garbanzo beans)

corn tortillas (check the label)

gluten-free oats

kidney beans

lentils

quinoa

GLUTEN-FREE FLOURS

almond flour (or ground almonds)

brown rice flour

cornflour (cornstarch)

gluten-free flour blends

hazelnut (cob nut) flour

millet flour

oat flour (check the label)

potato flour

quinoa flour

soy flour

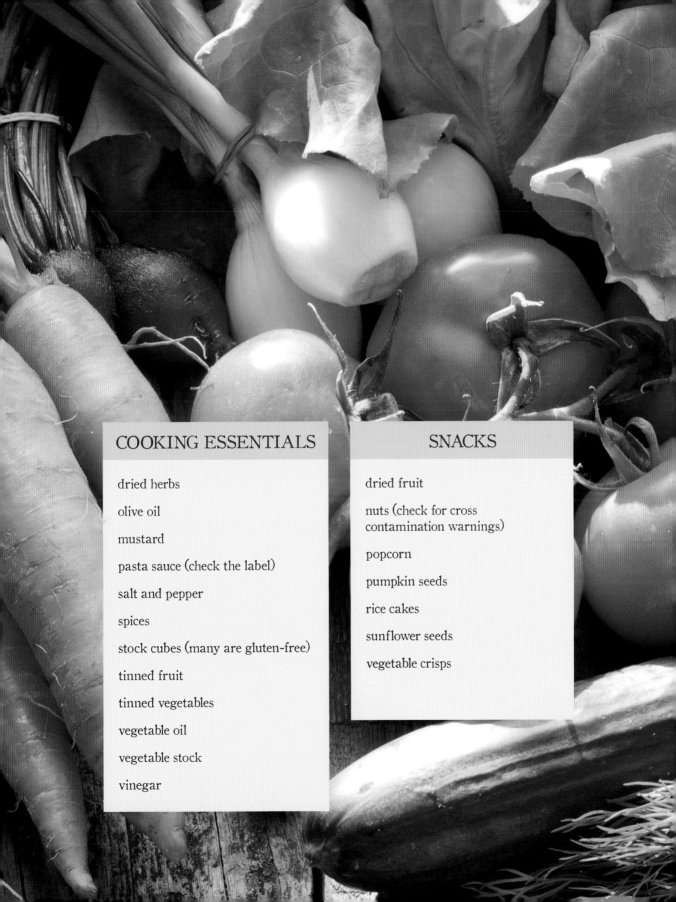

COOKING ESSENTIALS

dried herbs

olive oil

mustard

pasta sauce (check the label)

salt and pepper

spices

stock cubes (many are gluten-free)

tinned fruit

tinned vegetables

vegetable oil

vegetable stock

vinegar

SNACKS

dried fruit

nuts (check for cross contamination warnings)

popcorn

pumpkin seeds

rice cakes

sunflower seeds

vegetable crisps

Once your store cupboard is stocked, you can buy the perishable ingredients that you'll need to cook your gluten-free meals. Many of these foods are naturally gluten-free and there are plenty to choose from! This list is just a start:

VEGETABLES

- asparagus
- beansprouts
- broccoli
- carrots
- curly kale
- onions
- peppers
- potatoes
- spinach
- squash
- sweet potatoes

FRUITS

- apples
- bananas
- berries
- citrus fruit
- mangoes
- pears

MEAT AND PROTEIN

bacon

beef

chicken

eggs

fish

lamb

pork

shellfish

MILK AND DAIRY

cheese (check the label on shredded cheese)

milk

sour cream

yogurt (check the label)

If you're on a budget, plan ahead and make use of your freezer. You can make big batches of dishes such as bolognese sauce and freeze the leftovers. You can also make use of multi-buy offers on meat, and freeze what you don't need straight away.

KEEP IT FRESH

One downside to gluten-free food substitutes, such as bread, is that they usually don't contain the preservatives used in regular bread. This means that they can dry out more quickly, so you need to store them properly. Once opened, keep them in an airtight container in a dark, dry place. You can refrigerate them to make them last longer and you can even keep your bread in the freezer.

Keeping it off

Congratulations – you've done it! You've stuck to the gluten-free diet and are feeling the benefits already. You've got more energy, you feel great and you've lost some weight.

Now comes the next challenge: keeping it off. Many dieters reach their target and then lose the motivation to stick with the new routine, putting the weight straight back on again. It doesn't have to happen to you. Here are a few tips for keeping motivated:

- Remember why you did it! Have a look at an old photo of yourself, or look back at your food diary. Think about how you felt before cutting out gluten and focus on how much better you're feeling – and looking – now.

- Set a new target. For example, now that you're healthier and fitter, maybe you could train for a fun run or even a half marathon. Keeping focused on goals can help stop you from backtracking.

- Don't get stuck in a rut. Set yourself the goal of trying two or three new gluten-free recipes every week.

- If you've gone down a size, clear out some of your old clothes and treat yourself to a few things in your new size.

- Keep track. If you have a target weight, weigh yourself once a week to help you stay on track.

- Set an example. Your friends and family will notice how much better you're looking and feeling. Helping someone else to go gluten-free can keep you motivated to stick with it yourself.

The important thing is not to see a gluten-free diet as a 'quick fix'. It's a long-term lifestyle change that should leave you happier, fitter and healthier. Before long, you won't even miss the foods you've eliminated!

Diet consultant: Jo Stimpson

Written by: Ruth Manning

Picture Credits

All imagery: © iStock / Getty